The Grosvenor House Art & Antiques Fair

£7

12TH - 21ST JUNE 1997

Presented by
GROSVENOR HOUSE (PARK LANE) LTD

in association with
THE BRITISH ANTIQUE DEALERS' ASSOCIATION

1997 HANDBOOK

Published in association with Harpers & Queen

FOREWORD

I would like to welcome you to the 1997 Grosvenor House Art & Antiques Fair. This year, in celebration of the golden wedding of Her Majesty The Queen and His Royal Highness The Duke of Edinburgh, the Fair has mounted a special loan exhibition with a 'golden' theme, and we are most grateful to Her Majesty The Queen, and to Her Majesty Queen Elizabeth The Queen Mother, for providing the highlights of our exhibition by graciously lending items from the Royal Collections. We also welcome generous loans from The Worshipful Company of Goldsmiths for this important display.

It was in 1937, only three years after the inception of the Antique Dealers' Fair and Exhibition at Grosvenor House, that Queen Mary bestowed her patronage on the fledgling Fair. We therefore celebrate 60 years of Royal patronage and offer grateful thanks to Her Majesty Queen Elizabeth The Queen Mother who has been our Patron for much of this period.

The Imperial Cancer Research Fund is surely one of the best known of charities, and, as the beneficiary of this year's Charity Gala Evening, we hope it will raise a record amount. At a time when all things genetic are so topical, we are particularly glad that the charity's Director-General, Dr Paul Nurse, has written for us a brief explanation of the genetic basis of cancer – the new frontier on which this battle is fought (page 13).

The Victoria and Albert Museum is among our best-loved institutions, and its British Galleries perhaps the most-trodden of all. At the Loan Exhibition on the British Antique Dealers' Association stand, visitors to the Fair can enjoy a chance to see some of the most famous treasures, many of which will go into store when the museum undertakes its biggest redevelopment project ever. Most spectacular of all is the Kimbolton Cabinet, designed by Robert Adam, which features on the cover of this book. Dr Alan Borg, Director of the V&A, explains the project on page 8.

The 1997 Foreword to this Handbook would not be complete without a mention of George Levy, MBE, who died in September 1996. George Levy's contribution to the Fair has been unsurpassed. His company, H. Blairman & Sons, has exhibited at Grosvenor House since 1938, and he was a member of the Executive Committee from 1972 until his death. From personal experience, I know that he only had one standard – and that was second to none. He is much missed by those of us who were privileged to work with him.

We are, as ever, most grateful to the Director of the Fair, Alison Vaissière, and her staff, for all their hard work throughout the year, and to the Fair's Executive Committee for its help. We look forward to a splendid Fair, and hope very much that you will enjoy your visit.

Anthony Spink

Anthony Spink
Chairman

CONTENTS

PATRON

OF

THE GROSVENOR HOUSE ART & ANTIQUES FAIR

Her Majesty Queen Elizabeth The Queen Mother

A GOLDEN DISPLAY IN THE GREAT ROOM

This year sees the 50th anniversary of the marriage of Her Majesty The Queen to His Royal Highness The Duke of Edinburgh. We are delighted to mark this 'golden' wedding with the exhibition of spectacular objects of silver-gilt, most graciously lent by Her Majesty The Queen, and by Her Majesty Queen Elizabeth The Queen Mother. The 'golden' theme is further reflected in objects generously loaned by The Worshipful Company of Goldsmiths, two of which are shown here.

The Dürer Cup
A silver-gilt cup, the design attributed to A.W.N. Pugin and based on a design by Albrecht Dürer in the British Museum. Height 24.3 cm (9 ¹/₂ in).

This cup was made for George IV in 1826-27 by John Bridge, of Rundell Bridge and Rundell, at a cost of £150 2s 6d. It is one of a number of pieces of historicist plate purchased by George IV at the time that Windsor Castle was being transformed by Sir Jeffry Wyatville. Augustus Welby Northmore Pugin was first seen by one of the partners of Rundell Bridge and Rundell in the Print Room of the British Museum, copying prints by Dürer and others. He may well have designed this cup for the firm at the age of only fifteen.

Lent by Her Majesty The Queen

Photograph: The Royal Collection © 1997 Her Majesty The Queen

Above, one of a pair of silver-gilt dishes by Edward Wakelin, circa 1750, with borders of swirling flutes and panels of cast decoration comprising tiny shells. The splendidly engraved arms, possibly added in 1812, are those of George IV, who owned these dishes when Prince of Wales. Diameter 25.4 cm (10 in).

Lent by Her Majesty Queen Elizabeth The Queen Mother

Photograph: © 1997 Her Majesty Queen Elizabeth The Queen Mother

The Queen's Cup
Below, a silver-gilt cup and cover, designed by R.Y. Goodden, maker's mark Wakely & Wheeler Ltd., 1953. Height 48 cm (19 in). The cup is inscribed, 'The Coronation Cup of Her Majesty Queen Elizabeth II, 1953', and was commissioned by The Worshipful Company of Goldsmiths to commemorate the coronation. This followed the tradition of a cup, given to the Company by Sir Martin Bowes, from which Queen Elizabeth I drank after her coronation. Sir Martin, who was the Lord Mayor, as well as Chief Butler and Prime Warden of the Company, attended the coronation. HM Queen Elizabeth II drank a toast to The City of London from the present cup at a banquet in The Mansion House in 1954 held to commemorate her return, with HRH The Duke of Edinburgh, from a royal tour of the Commonwealth. This banquet is recorded in the painting by Terence Cuneo entitled *Mansion House 19th May 1954*, owned by the Company, which also forms part of this loan display.
Reproduced by courtesy of The Worshipful Company of Goldsmiths

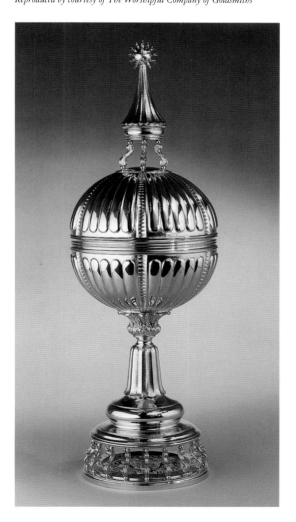

Top, and detail above, a silver-gilt steeple cup and cover by Robert Stocker, 1886. Height 76 cm (30 in). Every part of the plain strap-work is engraved with inscriptions chronicling events in Queen Victoria's reign. Near the hallmark on the lid (see detail) are recorded the Queen opening the Albert Hall on March 29th, 1871, the death of Sir John Herschel, Astronomer, on May 11th, 1871, and the recovery of her son, The Prince of Wales, from typhoid fever on December 14th, 1871. Events as diverse as assassination attempts on The Queen herself, the death of Charles Dickens, the Irish Land Bill, and the foundation of the Post Office, are noted elsewhere on the cup.
Reproduced by courtesy of The Worshipful Company of Goldsmiths

NEW GALLERIES FOR A NEW MILLENNIUM

This year's loan exhibition at The Grosvenor House Art & Antiques Fair offers a chance to see some of the greatest treasures from the Victoria and Albert Museum, many of which will go into store when the museum embarks on its most ambitious project to date. Dr Alan Borg, Director of the V&A, explains.

Figure 1   The Kimbolton Cabinet, designed by Robert Adam (1728 - 1792) and made by Ince and Mayhew. Mahogany and oak, with marquetry of various woods, inset panels of pietre dure *dating from 1709, and ormolu mounts by Matthew Boulton. English, circa 1775. Height 189cm (74 ¹/₂ in).*

Everyone is now thinking about the millennium, and at the Victoria and Albert Museum we are planning, appropriately, to look both forward and back. Looking forward will be the dramatic new building on our Boilerhouse site, which is to hold the new collections of the 21st century and to explore the new world that information technology is making possible. Designed by Polish-born architect Daniel Libeskind, the initial concept models for this provided one of the most controversial arts topics of 1996. However, no one should judge a building on the basis of a first concept model, especially not in the awful photographs which appeared in the press. Those of us closely involved in the project all believe that it will be a marvellous addition to the V&A and will come to be seen as one of the great museum buildings of our age. The founders of the V&A, including the Prince Consort, Henry Cole, and, a little later, William Morris, were all at the cutting edge of contemporary art and design. They would have demanded that any late 20th-century extension to their museum be in the most advanced style of the day. I do not think they would be disappointed with the Libeskind design.

But this is only one way in which we plan to mark the millennium. We have recently embarked upon the most ambitious display project ever undertaken by the museum. This is the re-presentation of the entire run of British Galleries, comprising what many people see as the core collections of the V&A and containing many of our greatest treasures. For this reason, I am delighted that the V&A is providing a loan exhibition to the British Antique Dealers' Association stand at The Grosvenor House Art & Antiques Fair this year. The V&A has always enjoyed a special relationship with the members of the BADA, and it is particularly appropriate that we should be joining them in exhibiting at the Fair. Some of the key pieces that will be shown in the new British Galleries are displayed here, so it is worth explaining why this project is important and necessary.

The British Galleries, still often called the English Primary Galleries, were last re-displayed just after the Second World War, when Leigh Ashton was Director. Resources were scarce, and the techniques of museum display were still somewhat primitive. Nonetheless, those displays have served generations of students, scholars, and

visitors well, but they are now simply worn out. They are also out of date. Scholarship, display methods, and the collections themselves have all advanced dramatically in the past 50 years and we are now in a position to do full justice to the spectacular objects we hold. Significantly, almost all the objects in the V&A exhibition at the Fair have been acquired by the museum since the Second World War. To put the whole task in perspective, it could be said to be the equivalent of creating and displaying an entire museum of moderate size all at one go.

Why must the work all be done at the same time? There are several reasons, but primarily it is because we have decided to install air-conditioning in these galleries in order to keep out the dirt, to safeguard the objects, and to protect our visitors. The galleries occupy two floors along the Aston Webb façade of the V&A facing Cromwell Road, the equivalent of a four-lane motorway, which makes this one of the most polluted areas of London. So, all the galleries will close next year, with the re-opening planned for 2001. Inevitably, while the work is in progress, many visitors will be disappointed to find their favourite objects not on

Figure 2   The Ashburnham Centrepiece by Nicholas Sprimont, bearing his mark. Silver. English, 1747. Height 46.5 cm (18 1/4 in).

Figure 3 The Girl-in-a-Swing. Soft-paste porcelain. English, circa 1749 - 1759. Height 16 cm (6 ¼ in).

Figure 4 Hogarth's dog, Trump. Soft-paste porcelain. English, circa 1747 - 1750. Height 12.4 cm (4 ⅞ in).

cost of the whole project is set at £31 million, and we need to raise around £8 million from private sponsors – so in part this article and the exhibition are an appeal for support.

To encourage and enthuse you, let me say a little about some of the important objects we are displaying at the Fair. The largest and most obvious is the Kimbolton Cabinet, a key piece of English furniture, designed by Robert Adam to display eleven Florentine *pietre dure* panels (*Figure 1*). The panels, depicting romantic seascapes, and mountainous pastoral scenes, were made by Baccio Cappelli in 1709. They were acquired some time later by a member of the Montagu family, and, around 1771, the Duchess of Manchester commissioned Robert Adam to design a cabinet to hold them, for Kimbolton Castle. It was made by Ince and Mayhew, with fine ormolu mounts by Boulton and Fothergill. Illustrated in many textbooks of design, it is generally recognised as one of the touchstones of British 18th-century furniture. When it was acquired by the V&A in 1949, the cabinet was immediately displayed in the new English Primary Galleries. It will have an equally prominent place in the new British Galleries.

No less spectacular is the Ashburnham Centrepiece by Nicholas Sprimont (*Figure 2*). Once owned by John, 2nd Earl of Ashburnham, whose arms are engraved on it, it is one of the masterworks of English rococo silver. Sprimont, born in Belgium, worked in both silver and porcelain and in the following year, 1748, was appointed manager of the newly founded Chelsea porcelain factory. This elaborate centrepiece, with its pierced, covered bowl resting on two kids, echoes a design of two hundred years earlier for a salt cellar by Giulio Romano. A similar theme was

view, but this sacrifice will be worthwhile. We shall be able to present new displays that will be unrivalled in the world, covering four centuries of decorative art, from the accession of King Henry VII to the death of Queen Victoria. The famous historic rooms will be restored and re-displayed as proper rooms, not stage sets, which the visitor can enter and experience. For the first time, it will be possible to include textiles on a large scale, along with all the other decorative arts, representing the luxurious panoply of British social life in all its rich diversity.

The new galleries will be designed to cater for the needs of all our audiences, young and old, knowledgeable or not, and with half an hour or half a day to spend. We are undertaking an unprecedented research programme into the needs of our visitors, and we shall produce displays that are educational in the broadest and best sense. None of this will be possible without the help of the National Heritage Lottery Fund, which has allowed so many new initiatives to go forward. However, the

used on a centrepiece made for the Duke of Somerset by Sprimont's neighbour in Soho, Paul Crespin, in 1746. The relationship between the two pieces has been much debated by scholars. The V&A centrepiece bears Sprimont's mark, but it seems probable that Crespin had a hand in it.

When the Ashburnham silver was sold in 1914, the centrepiece was purchased by an American collector, but the museum was able to buy it back in 1971, with the assistance of the National Art Collections Fund.

It is interesting to see the Ashburnham Centrepiece alongside the porcelain figurine of the Girl-in-a-Swing (*Figure 3*), since the latter was attributed to Nicholas Sprimont's new Chelsea factory, when it was given to the museum in 1922. It is now thought to be the product of a rival factory of unknown location, set up by Charles Gouyn, a jeweller with premises in St James's, London, who had worked as a partner in Sprimont's Chelsea factory until some time before March, 1749. This attribution is the result of research carried out by curators at the V&A and is typical of the way in which the scope of the collections and the expertise of the staff often combine to increase our knowledge of the history of decorative art.

Nicholas Sprimont is also linked to the well-known Chelsea porcelain figure of Hogarth's dog, Trump (*Figure 4*). This much-loved pet was sculpted in terracotta by Roubiliac, to go with his bust of the painter which is now in the National Portrait Gallery. Although the terracotta Trump is lost, the porcelain version links Hogarth, Roubiliac, and Sprimont, and provides a vivid illustration of the interconnections between those artists who congregated at Slaughter's Coffee House and at St Martin's Lane Academy in Soho, and who pioneered the rococo style in England.

The final exhibit I would like to highlight, a Bow porcelain chocolate- or coffee-pot of circa 1760-65 (*Figure 5*), shows the development of this English rococo style to its exuberant extreme, and is also a relatively recent arrival in the museum, which acquired it in 1993. It is much closer to continental models than the earlier English work, recalling especially the Italian porcelain factory at Doccia. Significantly, a Doccia service is recorded in the sale of the Bow warehouse in 1764. This pot is no mere copy of an Italian model, however, but represents a distinctive English interpretation of the florid continental motifs.

The stylistic and historical links between many of the pieces displayed in this small exhibition give a glimpse of the sort of interconnections which will be demonstrated throughout the new British Galleries. They will show how British art and design evolved, over these centuries, from a largely import-based and derivative culture to one in which British design literally led the world. It is an

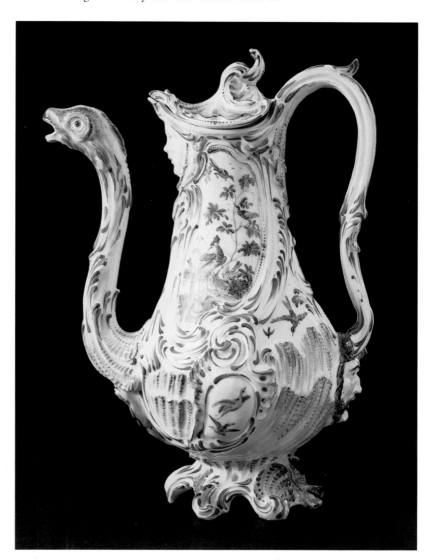

exciting and dramatic story, full of glorious objects and wonders of workmanship. I believe the achievement of these new galleries is a vitally important way of marking the start of the new millennium by looking back at some of Britain's greatest achievements in the previous era.

Figure 5 A chocolate- or coffee-pot. Soft-paste porcelain (Bow factory), painted in enamels. English, circa 1760 - 1765. Height 30.5 cm (12 in).

The Victoria and Albert Museum, South Kensington, London SW7 2RL Tel: 0171-938 8500

THE CHARITY GALA EVENING

The Grosvenor House Art & Antiques Fair is delighted to host the Charity Gala Evening on Thursday 12th June. The Gala will be held in the presence of Her Royal Highness Princess Alexandra, GCVO, President of the Imperial Cancer Research Fund, the charity chosen to benefit from this prestigious event.

A Chinese theme has been adopted for the Gala, in recognition of a milestone in the history of Hong Kong as the colony reverts to Chinese rule. We are most grateful to Dr T. T. Tsui, who has generously agreed to sponsor the evening.

We would also like to extend our thanks to Champagne Palmer for its assistance and to the Patrons, Benefactors, and Committee members, without whose support the Charity Gala Evening would not be possible. We are particularly grateful to Jennifer d'Abo and David Tang, the Gala's Co-Chairmen, for their enthusiasm and support.

For many years, this exclusive event has raised substantial sums of money for charity – last year over £190,000 was raised in support of two children's charities. We confidently hope that this year we can once more turn the enjoyment of a special evening to the account of a very worthwhile cause.

HRH Princess Alexandra discusses the work of the Imperial Cancer Research Fund

THE GENETIC BASIS OF CANCER

by Dr Paul Nurse FRS
Director-General of the Imperial Cancer
Research Fund

Our bodies are made up of cells and all growth occurs by these cells undergoing repeated rounds of division. This takes place all the time in a healthy person, for example during the growth of a child, or when a damaged part of the body is repaired. Controls operate which ensure that cells only undergo division when it is correct to do so, such as during growth or wound healing. However, when these controls become defective, cells can multiply out of control, forming disorganised masses of cells which make up a tumour.

All the activities of cells are determined by the many thousands of genes located on the chromosomes which are passed on from cell to cell every time division takes place. Among these genes there is a sub-set numbering around 200 which are important for controlling cell growth and division. When these particular genes become damaged, the controls governing growth and division become defective, leading to uncontrolled cell multiplication. Because each newly-formed cell receives damaged copies of the genes, all the cells produced are also out of control, and so go on to divide. This is the genetic basis of cancer.

At the Imperial Cancer Research Fund, we have a major research programme investigating the genes which cause cancer. We want to identify the members of the sub-set of genes which, when damaged, result in uncontrolled cell multiplication. Once we have identified them, we need to find out how they work, both in healthy and in cancerous cells. This will greatly improve our understanding of this very complicated disease. It will allow us to identify which genes have become damaged in a specific cancer, and how these defects have upset the normal controls acting over cell growth and cell division.

With this information we will be able to describe very precisely the changes that have occurred in a specific cancer and, as a consequence, develop ways to optimise treatment. It will be possible to devise novel ways by which we can correct the defective operation of the damaged genes. The goal will be to produce far more specific treatments that influence only the defective controls, and have little effect on all the other activities within cells. In this way, adverse side-effects can be avoided, generating more effective and less unpleasant ways of treating cancer. Our skilled scientists and doctors at the Imperial Cancer Research Fund already have the tools and techniques necessary to carry out this work. What we need now are the resources to develop fully this important research programme.

Imperial Cancer
Research Fund

Amanda Harbottle,
National Events Committee,
Fundraising Department,
61 Lincoln's Inn Fields,
London WC2A 3PX
Tel: 0171-269 3178
Fax: 0171-269 3273

THE GROSVENOR HOUSE
ART & ANTIQUES FAIR

THE EXECUTIVE
COMMITTEE

Konrad Bernheimer
Elaine Dean
Peter French
Martin Levy
Penny Marks
Henry Neville
Nicolas Norton
David Pettifer
Gerry Robinson
Peter Schaffer
Anthony Spink
Alison Vaissière
Johnny Van Haeften
Anthony Woodburn

THE VETTING
COMMITTEES

Chairman of Vetting:
David Pettifer

Arms & Armour
John Anderson
Claude Blair
Michael German
John Harding
Nicholas McCullough

Carpets, Rugs & Textiles
Michael Franses
Mansour Heskia
Alexander Juran
Joe Mayorcas
Leon Sassoon
Jacqueline Simcox
Lanto Synge
Antoine de Vermoutier

*Clocks, Watches, Barometers
& Scientific Instruments*
Simon Bull
David J. Bryden
John Carlton-Smith
Richard Garnier
John de Haan
Beresford Hutchinson
Stephen Jarrett
Rodney Law
Daniel Parkes
Sebastian Whitestone
Anthony Woodburn
Harriet Wynter

European Ceramics
William F.A. Buck
Kate Foster
Jonathan Horne
Betty Klaber
Pamela Klaber
Stafford Lorie
Hugo Morley-Fletcher
Pearl Manheim
Alistair Sampson
Angela Gräfin von Wallwitz
Mary Wise

*European Sculpture, Works of
Art & Antiquities*
William Agnew
Joanna Barnes
Anna Bennett
Richard Falkiner
Jonathan Harris
Edward Horswell
Alastair Laing
Elizabeth Wilson

Furniture & Architectural Items
Bernard Apter
Terry Baxter
Jean Gismondi
Michael Hill
John Hill
Tobias Jellinek
Andrew Jenkins
Martin Levy
Melvyn Lipitch
Robert Luck
Baden Marston
Christopher Payne
Jacques Perrin
Antony Preston
Brian Rolleston
Alan Rubin
Jacob Stodel
Thomas Woodham-Smith

Glass
Andrew Burne
Martin Mortimer
Timothy Osborne
Julia Schottlander
John P. Smith

*Glass Pictures, Tôle
& Papier Mâché*
Peter F. Cheek
Martin Levy
Lanto Synge

Icons
Lawrence Morrocco
Martyn Saunders-Rawlins
Richard Temple

*Jewellery, Bijouterie, Fabergé,
Snuff Boxes, Miniatures
& Enamels*
Susan Benjamin
Claude Blair
Shirley Bury
Walter Hakim
Anthony Landsberg
David Lavender
Nigel Norman
Jonathan Norton
Martin Norton
Alexander von Solodkoff
Charles Truman

*Later 19th- & 20th-Century
Western Applied Arts*
Jonathan Harris
John Jesse
Martin Levy
Clive Wainwright
Michael Whiteway

Metalware
Roderick Butler
Michael Crowther
Belinda Gentle
Peter Gould
Brand Inglis
Andrew Jenkins

Numismatics
Richard Falkiner

*Oriental Ceramics, Furniture
& Works of Art*
John Anderson
Richard Barker
Anthony Carter
Paul Champkins
David Freedman
Michael Gillingham
John Harding
Roger Keverne
Jeremy Knowles
Richard Marchant
Michael Spink
Clemens Vanderven
Douglas Wright
Grace Wu Bruce

Ormolu
John Hill
Robin Kern
Didier Leblanc
Martin Levy
Jacob Stodel

*Paintings, Watercolours
& Drawings*
Christopher Bibby
William Drummond
Andrew Edmunds
David Fuller
Jonathan Green
John Hayes
Alan Hobart
Richard Knight
Lowell Libson
Gabriel Naughton
Kate de Rothschild
John Sabin
Anthony Speelman
Rafael Valls
Johnny Van Haeften
Alex Wengraf
Clovis Whitfield
Christopher Wood

*Prints, Maps, Books &
Manuscripts*
Andrew Edmunds
Sam Fogg
Thomas Heneage
John Maggs
Katharina Mayer Haunton
Raymond O'Shea
John Sabin

Silver & Sheffield Plate
John Bourdon-Smith
Alastair Dickenson
Brand Inglis
Francis Norton
Nicolas Norton
Tim Schroder
Hugh Tait

Treen & Bygones
Polly de Courcy Ireland
Anthony Foster
Andrew Jenkins
Celia Jennings
Baden Marston

OPENING TIMES:

The Fair will be open to the public between 12th and 21st June at the following times:
Thursday 12th June: 11.00 a.m. to 5.00 p.m.
Other weekdays: 11.00 p.m. to 8.00 p.m.
Weekends: 11.00 a.m. to 6.00 p.m.

GENERAL INFORMATION:

Visitors and Exhibitors are reminded that, in accordance with Westminster City Council regulations, money may not change hands on Sunday 15th June.

None of Granada Plc, Grosvenor House (Park Lane) Ltd, the Executive and Vetting Committees of the Fair or the Publishers of the 1997 Handbook in any way hold themselves responsible for, or warrant the genuineness or age of, any article exhibited or illustrated. Nevertheless, visitors and readers are requested to note that all articles exhibited or illustrated have been submitted for inspection to the Vetting Committees appointed to ensure that, as far as possible, the items conform to the regulations laid down for the conduct of the Fair.

The illustrations on the following pages have been submitted by Exhibitors as examples of the type of antique or work of art in which they deal and the items illustrated are not necessarily on view at the Fair.

The information contained in these pages was deemed to be correct at the time of going to press.

All exhibits, except for special loans, are for sale and articles sold at the Fair are replaced daily.

Visitors are respectfully reminded that, in the interests of security, not a single exhibit can be allowed out of the Fair unless it is accompanied by an official Pass-Out form.

ACKNOWLEDGMENTS:

The Organisers of The 1997 Grosvenor House Art & Antiques Fair wish to thank the Fair Executive Committee and the Vetting Committees for their invaluable support and co-operation.

Our thanks are extended to the Imperial Cancer Research Fund for its efforts and assistance with the Charity Gala Evening. We should also like to express our gratitude to the Committee Members, Sponsors, Patrons and Benefactors for their support of the Gala Evening.

Special thanks go to Elaine Dean, Secretary General of The British Antique Dealers' Association and to Hiscox Underwriting Limited and Needham, Jobson Insurance Brokers Limited for their sponsorship of the BADA stand. We are indebted, too, to George Carter, who has been responsible for the design of the Fair, and also to Janet Turner, Fair Lighting Consultant, for her expertise and guidance.

The Fair is most grateful to Champagne Palmer, for its sponsorship of The Champagne Palmer Bar created by The Romantic Garden Nursery of Norwich, Norfolk, with furniture and carpets supplied by Lloyd Loom of Spalding and Firth Carpets respectively. Thanks also to Domaine de Triennes for its sponsorship of The V&A Bar and to The Champagne Company for its sponsorship of The Champagne Co. Bar. The music throughout the Fair is by courtesy of Deutsche Grammophon with equipment loaned by Philips Consumer Electronics.

Thanks are also extended to Seago which has kindly loaned various pieces of garden sculpture to enhance the Fair.

Finally, we should like to thank Anthony Spink, past President of The British Antique Dealers' Association, for his role as Chairman of the Fair.

ORGANISED BY:

Director: Alison Vaissière
Administrator: Lucy Head
Secretary: Olivia Powell
Consultants: Samantha Clarke, Jocelyn Poulton
on behalf of Grosvenor House (Park Lane) Ltd.,
Grosvenor House, Park Lane, London W1A 3AA.
Telephone: 0171-499 6363 Extension 4596/4872
Facsimile: 0171-495 8747
Web site: http://www.grosvenor-fair.co.uk
Email: grosvenor-antiquesfair@msn.com

Title page photograph and endpapers:
The Kimbolton Cabinet, English, circa 1775, designed by Robert Adam, made by Ince and Mayhew.
The Victoria and Albert Museum.

Photographs:
Her Majesty Queen Elizabeth The Queen Mother.
Courtesy of Camera Press Ltd.
pages 12 & 13: courtesy of
the Imperial Cancer Research Fund.

THE 1997 HANDBOOK:

Published by *Harpers & Queen*
The National Magazine Company Ltd.

Editor: Deborah Scott
Design: Robert Wakely, Image Design Group
Production Managers: Alan Boxall, Geoff Lanegan
Production Assistant: Marya Armanazi
Advertising : Sue Colomb, Juliette Wood
Joint Publishers: Jamie Bill, *Harpers & Queen*
Guilluame Collis, Oyster Publishing Ltd.

Printed by: Jarrolds Book Printing, Thetford, Norfolk
Colour Reproduction by: Graphic Facilities, London

© Grosvenor House (Park Lane) Ltd.

OPENING PREVIEW

The undermentioned kindly accepted invitations to the Opening Preview of the Fairs since 1934

1934   The Marchioness of Reading,
The Baroness Swanborough

1935   His Royal Highness The Duke of Kent

1936   The Earl of Athlone

1937   The Viscount Lee of Fareham

1938   The Marquess of Willingdon

1939   Her Royal Highness The Princess Royal

1947   Her Royal Highness Princess Alice,
Countess of Athlone

1948   Her Royal Highness The Princess Royal

1949   The Duke of Devonshire

1950   Her Royal Highness Princess Marina,
Duchess of Kent

1951   Her Royal Highness The Princess Elizabeth,
Duchess of Edinburgh, now
Her Majesty The Queen

1952   Lady Churchill, later Baroness Spencer-Churchill

1953   Her Royal Highness The Princess Margaret,
now Her Royal Highness The Princess Margaret,
Countess of Snowdon

1954   The Hon Winthrop W. Aldrich, when United
States Ambassador to The Court of St James

1955   The Countess Mountbatten of Burma

1956   Lady Eden, now The Countess of Avon

1957   Her Royal Highness The Duchess of Gloucester,
now Her Royal Highness The Princess Alice,
Duchess of Gloucester

1958   Her Royal Highness Princess Alexandra of Kent,
now Her Royal Highness Princess Alexandra,
the Hon Mrs Angus Ogilvy

1959   Senhor Francesco de Assis Chateaubriand,
when Brazilian Ambassador to The Court of
St James

1960   The Countess of Harewood,
now Mrs Jeremy Thorpe

1961   The Earl of Snowdon

1962   Her Grace The Duchess of Beaufort

1963   The Lord Mayor of London (Sir Ralph Perring)

1964   The Marchioness of Blandford

1965   Her Majesty Queen Elizabeth The Queen Mother

1966   His Highness The Aga Khan

1967   Her Royal Highness Princess Paola of Belgium

1968   His Royal Highness The Duke of Kent

1969   Her Royal Highness Princess Alexandra,
the Hon Mrs Angus Ogilvy

1970   Her Royal Highness The Princess Margaret,
Countess of Snowdon

1971   The Prime Minister The Rt Hon Edward Heath

1972   Her Royal Highness The Princess Anne,
now Her Royal Highness The Princess Royal

1973   Field-Marshall Sir Gerald Templer

1975   Her Royal Highness The Duchess of Kent

1976   The Lord Goodman

1977   The Rt Hon Margaret Thatcher

1977   Her Royal Highness Princess Alexandra,
the Hon Mrs Angus Ogilvy
The Burlington International Fine Art Fair

1978   Her Royal Highness The Duchess of Gloucester

1979   His Royal Highness The Duke of Edinburgh
The Somerset House Art Treasures Exhibition

1979   Their Royal Highnesses Prince and Princess
Michael of Kent
The Burlington International Fine Art Fair

1980   The Prime Minister The Rt Hon Margaret
Thatcher
The Burlington House Fair

1982   Her Royal Highness The Princess Margaret,
Countess of Snowdon
The Burlington House Fair

1983   Her Royal Highness The Princess Anne,
now Her Royal Highness The Princess Royal

1983   Her Royal Highness Princess Alexandra,
the Hon Mrs Angus Ogilvy
The Burlington House Fair

1984   The Duchess of Devonshire

1985   Her Royal Highness Princess Alexandra,
the Hon Mrs Angus Ogilvy

1985   Their Royal Highnesses The Prince and Princess
of Wales
The Burlington House Fair

1986   Her Royal Highness The Princess Margaret,
Countess of Snowdon

1987   Their Majesties King Constantine and
Queen Anne-Marie of The Hellenes

1987   Her Royal Highness The Duchess of Gloucester
The Burlington House Fair

1988   The Prime Minister
The Rt Hon Margaret Thatcher

1989   Her Royal Highness Princess Margriet
of The Netherlands

1990   His Royal Highness The Prince Edward

1991   The Rt Hon the Lord St John of Fawsley

1992   His Excellency the Honorable Raymond G.H. Seitz,
Ambassador of the United States of America

1993   The Prime Minister The Rt Hon John Major,
represented by Mrs John Major

1994   Her Royal Highness The Princess Royal

1995   Her Royal Highness The Duchess of York

ALPHABETICAL LIST OF EXHIBITORS

A La Vieille Russie, Inc
781 Fifth Avenue, New York
N.Y. 10022, U.S.A.
Tel. 212-752 1727 Fax. 212-223 6454
Email: alvr1@aol.com
Web site: http://www.dir-dd.com/alvr.html
Member: The National Antique & Art Dealers'
Association of America, Inc.
Member: Art and Antique Dealers' League of
America, Inc.
Fabergé, jewellery, silver, porcelain, icons,
paintings.
STAND NO. 65
STAND TEL. 0171-499 6363 *Ext.* 7165
pages 248 - 251

Norman Adams Ltd
8-10 Hans Road, Knightsbridge,
London SW3 1RX
(opposite west side Harrods)
Tel. 0171-589 5266 Fax. 0171-589 1968
Member: British Antique Dealers' Association
18th-century English furniture, clocks and
barometers, glass pictures and chandeliers.
STAND NO. 47
STAND TEL. 0171-499 6363 *Ext.* 7147
pages 90 - 93

William Agnew
58 Englefield Road, London N1 4HA
Tel. and Fax. 0171-254 7429
Member: British Antique Dealers' Association
European sculpture and works of art, maiolica and
pottery.
(By appointment only)
STAND NO. 9
STAND TEL. 0171-499 6363 *Ext.* 7109
page 74

Luís Alegria
Av Dr Antunes Guinmares - 142,
4100 Porto, Portugal
Tel. 351-2 6182324 Fax. 351-2 6105446
Chinese export porcelain and European furniture.
STAND NO. 39
STAND TEL. 0171-499 6363 *Ext.* 7139
pages 94 - 95, 164

Apter-Fredericks Ltd
265-267 Fulham Road, London SW3 6HY
Tel. 0171-352 2188 Fax: 0171-376 5619
Member: British Antique Dealers' Association
18th-century English furniture.
STAND NO. 78
STAND TEL. 0171-499 6363 *Ext.* 7178
pages 96 - 98

Aronson Antiquairs
Nieuwe Spiegelstraat 39 - 1017 DC Amsterdam,
The Netherlands
Tel. 31-20 6233103 Fax. 31-20 6383066
Web site: http://www.aronson.nl
Member: TEFAF - European Fine Art Foundation
Member: Confédération Internationale
des Négociants en Œuvres d'Art
17th- and 18th-century Dutch delftware, Chinese
porcelain, Continental furniture and silver.
STAND NO. 61
STAND TEL. 0171-499 6363 *Ext.* 7161
pages 56 - 59

Asprey
165-169 New Bond Street,
London W1Y 0AR
Tel. 0171-493 6767 Fax. 0171-491 0384
Member: British Antique Dealers' Association
Clocks and barometers, furniture, glass, jewellery
and snuff-boxes, silver and Old Sheffield Plate,
Russian works of art, ceramics.
STAND NO. 11
STAND TEL. 0171-499 6363 *Ext.* 7111
pages 48, 62, 99, 252

Avon Antiques
25, 26, 27 Market Street, Bradford on Avon,
Wiltshire BA15 1LL
Tel. 01225 862052 Fax. 01225 862937
Member: British Antique Dealers' Association
Furniture, clocks and barometers, metalwork,
textiles, treen.
STAND NO. 86
STAND TEL. 0171-499 6363 *Ext.* 7186
pages 100 - 102

Joanna Barnes Fine Arts
14 Mason's Yard, Duke Street, St James's,
London SW1Y 6BU
Tel. 0171-930 4215 Fax. 0171-839 8307
European sculpture from the 17th century to the
early 20th century.
STAND NO. 3
STAND TEL. 0171-499 6363 *Ext.* 7103
pages 76 - 77

H.C. Baxter & Sons
40 Drewstead Road, London SW16 1AB
Tel. 0181-769 5969 Fax. 0181-769 0898
Member: British Antique Dealers' Association
18th-century English furniture.
STAND NO. 24
STAND TEL. 0171-499 6363 *Ext.* 7124
pages 104 - 105

Michele Beiny, Inc
53 East 82nd Street, New York,
N.Y. 10028, U.S.A.
Tel. 212-794 9357 Fax. 212-772 0119
London Office: 0171-723 0456
Member: Art & Antique Dealers' League of America Inc.
18th- and early 19th-century European porcelain
and pottery, French furniture and decorative
objects, objets de vertu.
(By appointment only)
STAND NO. 84
STAND TEL. 0171-499 6363 *Ext.* 7184
pages 60 - 61

Konrad O. Bernheimer Ltd
1 Mount Street, London W1Y 5AA
Tel. 0171-495 7028 Fax. 0171-495 7027
Member: British Antique Dealers' Association
Member: Society of London Art Dealers
Old Master paintings, Continental furniture,
Oriental ceramics.
(By appointment only)
STAND NO. 62
STAND TEL. 0171-499 6363 *Ext.* 7162
pages 188 - 190

H. Blairman & Sons Ltd
119 Mount Street, London W1Y 5HB
Tel. 0171-493 0444 Fax. 0171-495 0766
Member: British Antique Dealers' Association
Furniture, works of art.
STAND NO. 53
STAND TEL. 0171-499 6363 *Ext.* 7153
pages 106 - 107

J.H. Bourdon-Smith Ltd
24 Mason's Yard, Duke Street, St James's,
London SW1Y 6BU
Tel. 0171-839 4714 Fax. 0171-839 3951
Member: British Antique Dealers' Association
Antique silver.
STAND NO. 75
STAND TEL. 0171-499 6363 *Ext.* 7175
pages 254 - 255

The British Antique Dealers' Association
20 Rutland Gate, London SW7 1BD
Tel. 0171-589 4128 Fax. 0171-581 9083
Established in 1918 to promote, protect and
further the interests of the antiques trade. The
BADA currently represents approximately 400 of
the most knowledgeable antique dealers in the
United Kingdom.
STAND NO. 2
STAND TEL. 0171-499 6363 *Ext.* 7102
page 24

John Carlton-Smith
17 Ryder Street, St James's,
London SW1Y 6PY
Tel. 0171-930 6622 Fax. 0171-930 9719
Member: British Antique Dealers' Association
Fine antique clocks and barometers.
STAND NO. 55
STAND TEL. 0171-499 6363 *Ext.* 7155
pages 46 - 47

Antoine Chenevière Fine Arts
27 Bruton Street, London W1X 7DB
Tel. 0171-491 1007 Fax. 0171-495 6173
Member: British Antique Dealers' Association
Russian furniture and objects.
STAND NO. 54
STAND TEL. 0171-499 6363 *Ext.* 7154
pages 75, 103

Richard Courtney Ltd
112-114 Fulham Road, London SW3 6HU
Tel. and Fax. 0171-370 4020
Member: British Antique Dealers' Association
18th-century English furniture.
STAND NO. 32
STAND TEL. 0171-499 6363 *Ext.* 7132
pages 108 - 111

Devenish & Company
929 Madison Avenue, New York,
N.Y. 10021, U.S.A.
Tel. 212-535 2888 Fax. 212-535 2889
Member: Art & Antique Dealers' League of America, Inc.
English and French 18th-century furniture,
paintings, objets d'art.
STAND NO. 71
STAND TEL. 0171-499 6363 *Ext.* 7171
pages 112 - 114

William Drummond
(Covent Garden Gallery Ltd.)
8 St James's Chambers, 2-10 Ryder Street,
London SW1Y 6QA
Tel. and Fax. 0171-930 9696
Member: British Antique Dealers' Association
Member: Society of London Art Dealers
18th- and 19th-century oil paintings, watercolours
and drawings.
(By appointment only)
STAND NO. 26
STAND TEL. 0171-499 6363 *Ext.* 7126
page 191

Andrew Edmunds
44 Lexington Street, London W1R 3LH
Tel. 0171-437 8594 Fax. 0171-439 2551
English and European prints, some drawings,
specialising in caricature and the 18th century.
STAND NO. 8
STAND TEL. 0171-499 6363 *Ext.* 7108
page 192

Sam Fogg
35 St George Street, London W1R 9FA
Tel. 0171-495 2333 Fax. 0171-409 3326
Member: Antiquarian Booksellers' Association
Medieval manuscripts and miniatures.
STAND NO. 49
STAND TEL. 0171-499 6363 *Ext.* 7149
pages 29 - 31

A. & E. Foster
Little Heysham, Naphill,
Buckinghamshire HP14 4SU
Tel. and Fax. 01494 562024
Member: British Antique Dealers' Association
Treen, works of art, metalwork.
(By appointment only)
STAND NO. 10
STAND TEL. 0171-499 6363 *Ext.* 7110
page 182

Michael Foster
118 Fulham Road, London SW3 6HU
Tel. 0171-373 3636 Fax. 0171-373 4042
Member: British Antique Dealers' Association
18th- and early 19th-century furniture, works of
art, musical instruments.
STAND NO. 40
STAND TEL. 0171-499 6363 *Ext.* 7140
pages 115 - 117

Victor Franses Gallery
57 Jermyn Street, St James's,
London SW1Y 6LX
Tel. 0171-493 6284 Fax. 0171-495 3668
Member: British Antique Dealers' Association
19th-century bronze animalier sculpture.
STAND NO. 30
STAND TEL. 0171-499 6363 *Ext.* 7130
pages 78 - 79

Gander & White Shipping Ltd
21 Lillie Road, London SW6 1UE
Tel. 0171-381 0571 Fax. 0171-381 5428
Packers and shippers.
STAND NO. 38
STAND TEL. 0171-499 6363 *Ext.* 7138
pages 268 - 269

Rupert Gentle Antiques
The Manor House, Milton Lilbourne,
Nr Pewsey, Wiltshire SN9 5LQ
Tel. 01672 563344 Fax. 01672 564136
Member: British Antique Dealers' Association
Metalwork, decorative objects, needlework.
STAND NO. 28
STAND TEL. 0171-499 6363 *Ext.* 7128
page 253

Galerie Gismondi
20 rue Royale, 75008 Paris, France
Tel. 33-1 42 60 73 89 Fax. 33-1 42 60 98 94
Member: Syndicat National des Antiquaires
17th- and 18th-century French furniture, Old
Master paintings.
STAND NO. 57
STAND TEL. 0171-499 6363 *Ext.* 7157
pages 118 - 119, 193

Michael Goedhuis
116 Mount Street, London W1Y 5HD
Tel. 0171-629 2228 Fax. 0171-409 3338
Member: British Antique Dealers' Association
Asian art and contemporary Chinese paintings.
STAND NO. 56
STAND TEL. 0171-499 6363 *Ext.* 7156
pages 162 - 163

Richard Green
44 Dover Street, London W1X 4JQ
39 Dover Street, London W1X 3RB
4 New Bond Street, London W1Y 0SP
33 New Bond Street, London W1Y 9HD
Tel. 0171-493 3939 Fax. 0171-629 2609
Member: British Antique Dealers' Association
Member: Society of London Art Dealers
Dutch and Flemish Old Masters, British sporting,
marine and 18th-century portraits, 19th-century
European, Victorian, Modern British and French
Impressionist and Post-Impressionist paintings.
STAND NO. 59
STAND TEL. 0171-499 6363 *Ext.* 7159
pages 194 - 197

Martyn Gregory
34 Bury Street, St James's,
London SW1Y 6AU
Tel. 0171-839 3731 Fax. 0171-930 0812
Member: British Antique Dealers' Association
Member: Society of London Art Dealers
British paintings and watercolours, China Trade
paintings and pictures relating to the Far East.
STAND NO. 79
STAND TEL. 0171-499 6363 *Ext.* 7179
pages 198 - 200

Grosvenor Antiques Ltd
27 Holland Street, Kensington,
London W8 4NA
Tel. 0171-937 8649 Fax. 0171-937 7179
Member: British Antique Dealers' Association
Porcelain, bronzes, Oriental and European small
works of art.
STAND NO. 48
STAND TEL. 0171-499 6363 *Ext.* 7148
pages 80, 165

Halcyon Days
14 Brook Street, London W1Y 1AA
Tel. 0171-629 8811 Fax. 0171-409 0280
and 4 Royal Exchange, London EC3V 3LL
Tel. 0171-626 1120
Member: British Antique Dealers' Association
Enamels, snuff boxes, objects of vertu, treen,
papier mâché, tôle peinte.
STAND NO. 35
STAND TEL. 0171-499 6363 *Ext.* 7135
pages 183, 256

Robert Hall
15c Clifford Street, Mayfair,
London W1X 1RF
Tel. 0171-734 4008 Fax. 0171-734 4408
Email: Robert Hall@www.desiderata.com
Member: British Antique Dealers' Association
Chinese works of art, specialising in Chinese snuff
bottles.
STAND NO. 20
STAND TEL. 0171-499 6363 *Ext.* 7120
pages 166 - 167

Hancocks & Company
1 Burlington Gardens, London W1X 2HP
Tel. 0171-493 8904 Fax. 0171-493 8905
Member: British Antique Dealers' Association
Fine period jewellery and silver, Art Nouveau, Art
Deco and signed 20th-century craftsmen items are
a particular speciality.
STAND NO. 31
STAND TEL. 0171-499 6363 *Ext.* 7131
pages 257 - 259

Jonathan Harris
9 Lower Addison Gardens,
London W14 8BG
Tel. 0171-602 6255 Fax. 0171-602 0488
Member: British Antique Dealers' Association
Member: Confédération Internationale
des Négociants en Œuvres d'Art
English, Oriental and European furniture and
works of art.
STAND NO. 69
STAND TEL. 0171-499 6363 *Ext.* 7169
pages 63, 120 - 121

Thomas Heneage Art Books
42 Duke Street, St James's,
London SW1Y 6DJ
Tel. 0171-930 9223 Fax. 0171-839 9223
Email: 100130.1050@compuserve.com
Art reference books and manuscripts, antiquities
and works of art, jewellery.
STAND NO. 15
STAND TEL. 0171-499 6363 *Ext.* 7115
page 32

Hotspur Ltd
14 Lowndes Street, London SW1X 9EX
Tel. 0171-235 1918 Fax. 0171-235 4371
Member: British Antique Dealers' Association
Furniture.
STAND NO. 60
STAND TEL. 0171-499 6363 *Ext.* 7160
pages 122 - 123

Iona Antiques
P.O. Box 285, London W8 6HZ
Tel. 0171-602 1193 Fax. 0171-371 2843
Member: British Antique Dealers' Association
19th-century primitive paintings of animals.
(By appointment only)
STAND NO. 29
STAND TEL. 0171-499 6363 *Ext.* 7129
page 201

Jeremy Ltd
29 Lowndes Street, London SW1X 9HX
Tel. 0171-823 2923 Fax. 0171-245 6197
Member: British Antique Dealers' Association
English and Continental furniture and works of
art.
STAND NO. 74
STAND TEL. 0171-499 6363 *Ext.* 7174
pages 124 - 127

C. John
70 South Audley Street, London W1Y 5FE
Tel. 0171-493 5288 Fax. 0171-409 7030
Member: British Antique Dealers' Association
Rugs, carpets, tapestries, needlework and textiles.
STAND NO. 80
STAND TEL. 0171-499 6363 *Ext.* 7180
pages 36 - 39

Klaber & Klaber
P.O. Box 9445, London NW3 1WD
Tel. 0171-435 6537 Fax. 0171-435 9459
Member: British Antique Dealers' Association
18th-century English and continental porcelain
and enamels.
(By appointment only)
STAND NO. 17
STAND TEL. 0171-499 6363 *Ext.* 7117
page 64

David Koetser Gallery
Talstrasse 37, 8001 Zurich, Switzerland
Tel. 41-1 211 5240 Fax. 41-1 211 5669
Member: Swiss Art Dealers' Association
Member: TEFAF - European Fine Art Foundation
17th-century Dutch and Flemish paintings,
14th to 18th-century Italian paintings.
STAND NO. 22
STAND TEL. 0171-499 6363 *Ext.* 7122
pages 202 - 203

D. S. Lavender (Antiques) Ltd
26 Conduit Street, London W1R 9TA
Tel. 0171-629 1782 Fax. 0171-629 3106
Member: British Antique Dealers' Association
Fine jewels, miniatures, works of art.
STAND NO. 33
STAND TEL. 0171-499 6363 *Ext.* 7133
pages 204 - 205, 260

Michael Lipitch Ltd
98 Fulham Road, London SW3 6HS
Tel. 0171-589 7327 Fax. 0171-823 9106
Member: British Antique Dealers' Association
Furniture and works of art.
STAND NO. 14
STAND TEL. 0171-499 6363 *Ext.* 7114
pages 128 - 131

Peter Lipitch Ltd
120 & 124 Fulham Road,
London SW3 6HU
Tel. 0171-373 3328 Fax. 0171-373 8888
Member: British Antique Dealers' Association
Furniture and mirrors.
STAND NO. 34
STAND TEL. 0171-499 6363 *Ext.* 7134
pages 132 - 133

Mallett
141 New Bond Street, London W1Y 0BS
Tel. 0171-499 7411 Fax. 0171-495 3179
and Bourdon House, 2 Davies Street, London
W1Y 1LJ
Tel. 0171-629 2444 Fax. 0171-499 2670
Member: British Antique Dealers' Association
English and Continental antique furniture and
objets d'art.
STAND NO. 12
STAND TEL. 0171-499 6363 *Ext.* 7112
pages 65, 134 - 136

Mallett Gallery
141 New Bond Street, London W1Y 0BS
Tel. 0171-499 7411 Fax. 0171-495 3179
Member: British Antique Dealers' Association
18th- and 19th-century paintings and
watercolours.
STAND NO. 5
STAND TEL. 0171-499 6363 *Ext.* 7105
pages 206 - 208

Mallett Glass
141 New Bond Street, London W1Y 0BS
Tel. 0171-499 7411 Fax. 0171-495 3179
Member: British Antique Dealers' Association
Antique glass.
STAND NO. 19
STAND TEL. 0171-499 6363 *Ext.* 7119
pages 66 - 67

S. Marchant & Son
120 Kensington Church Street,
London W8 4BH
Tel. 0171-229 5319 Fax. 0171-792 8979
Member: British Antique Dealers' Association
Chinese and Japanese ceramics, furniture, jades,
ivories, cloisonné and other works of art.
STAND NO. 43
STAND TEL. 0171-499 6363 *Ext.* 7143
pages 168 - 170

Mayorcas Ltd
8 Duke Street, St James's,
London SW1Y 6BN
Tel. 0171-839 3100 Fax. 0171-839 3223
Member: British Antique Dealers' Association
Member: Confédération Internationale des Négociants
en Œuvres d'Art
Member: Guild of Master Craftsmen
European textiles, tapestries, carpets and rugs.
STAND NO. 44
STAND TEL. 0171-499 6363 *Ext.* 7144
pages 40 - 41

Duncan R. Miller Fine Arts
17 Flask Walk, Hampstead,
London NW3 1HJ
Tel. 0171-435 5462 Fax. 0171-431 5352
Member: British Antique Dealers' Association
Member: Society of London Art Dealers
Modern British and European Impressionist and
Post-Impressionist paintings, the Scottish
Colourists.
STAND NO. 83
STAND TEL. 0171-499 6363 *Ext.* 7183
pages 209 - 211

Peter Nahum at
The Leicester Galleries Ltd
5 Ryder Street, London SW1Y 6PY
Tel. 0171-930 6059 Fax. 0171-930 4678
Paintings, drawings and sculpture for collectors
and museums including the Pre-Raphaelites.
STAND NO. 81
STAND TEL. 0171-499 6363 *Ext.* 7181
pages 212 - 214

Galerie Neuse Kunsthandel
Contrescarpe 14, 28203 Bremen, Germany
Tel. 49-421 32 56 42 Fax. 49-421 32 86 11
16th- to 19th-century European silver, 16th- to
18th-century works of art and *Kunstkammerstücke*,
16th- to 18th- century Old Master paintings and
Flemish and Brussels tapestries, 17th- to 18th-
century European furniture.
STAND NO. 23
STAND TEL. 0171-499 6363 *Ext.* 7123
pages 49, 81, 137, 215 .

Newhouse Galleries, Inc
19 East 66th Street, New York
N.Y. 10021, U.S.A.
Tel. 212-879 2700 Fax. 212-517 2680
Member: Art Dealers' Association of America Inc.
Member: The National Antique & Art Dealers'
Association of America, Inc.
Member: Syndicat National des Antiquaires
Négociants en Objets d'Art, Tableaux Anciens et
Modernes
Specialising in Old Master paintings, including
Dutch 17th-century, English 18th-century,
French 17th- and 18th- century, American
19th-century and Italian paintings of the 15th to
the 18th centuries.
STAND NO. 68
STAND TEL. 0171-499 6363 *Ext.* 7168
pages 216 - 218

Noortman
40-41 Old Bond Street, London W1X 4HP
Tel. 0171-491 7284 Fax. 0171-493 1570
Vrijthof 49, 6211 LE Maastricht, Holland
Tel. 31-43 321 6745 Fax. 31-43 321 3899
Member: Society of London Art Dealers
Old Master, 19th-century European,
Impressionist and Post-Impressionist paintings.
STAND NO. 42
STAND TEL. 0171-499 6363 *Ext.* 7142
pages 219 - 221

The O'Shea Gallery
120A Mount Street, Mayfair,
London W1Y 5HB
Tel. 0171-629 1122 Fax. 0171-629 1116
Member: British Antique Dealers' Association
Member: Antiquarian Booksellers' Association
15th- to 19th-century maps, topographical,
decorative, natural history, sporting and marine
prints, rare atlases and illustrated books, picture
frames.
STAND NO. 16
STAND TEL. 0171-499 6363 *Ext.* 7116
pages 222 - 223

Pelham Galleries Ltd
24-25 Mount Street, London W1Y 5RB
Tel. 0171-629 0905 Fax. 0171-495 4511
Member: British Antique Dealers' Association
Furniture, works of art, screens and architectural
decorations, early musical instruments.
STAND NO. 64
STAND TEL. 0171-499 6363 *Ext.* 7164
pages 138 - 140

Jacques et Patrick Perrin
98 rue du Faubourg Saint-Honoré,
75008 Paris, France
Tel. 33-1 42 65 01 38 Fax. 33-1 49 24 04 08
and 178 rue du Faubourg Saint-Honoré,
75008 Paris, France
Tel. 33-1 40 76 07 76 Fax. 33-1 40 76 09 37
Member: Syndicat National des Antiquaires
Négociants en Objets d'Art
18th-century French furniture, paintings,
drawings and sculpture.
STAND NO. 73
STAND TEL. 0171-499 6363 *Ext.* 7173
pages 68, 82 - 83

David Pettifer Ltd
219 King's Road, Chelsea, London SW3 5EJ
Tel. and Fax. 0171-352 3088
Member: British Antique Dealers' Association
Furniture.
STAND NO. 58
STAND TEL. 0171-499 6363 *Ext.* 7158
pages 141, 184

Trevor Philip & Sons Ltd
75A Jermyn Street, London SW1Y 6NP
Tel. 0171-930 2954 Fax. 0171-321 0212
Member: British Antique Dealers' Association
Scientific instruments including globes,
planetaria, barometers, microscopes and
architectural models.
STAND NO. 36
STAND TEL. 0171-499 6363 *Ext.* 7136
pages 50 - 51

Ronald Phillips Ltd
26 Bruton Street, London W1X 8LH
Tel. 0171-493 2341 Fax. 0171-495 0843
Member: British Antique Dealers' Association
18th-century and early 19th-century English
furniture, objets d'art and glass.
STAND NO. 82
STAND TEL. 0171-499 6363 *Ext.* 7182
pages 142 - 145

S. J. Phillips Ltd
139 New Bond Street, London W1A 3DL
Tel. 0171-629 6261/2 Fax. 0171-495 6180
Member: British Antique Dealers' Association
Jewellery, bijouterie and snuff-boxes, miniatures,
silver and Old Sheffield Plate.
STAND NO. 13
STAND TEL. 0171-499 6363 *Ext.* 7113
pages 262 - 265

Richard Philp
59 Ledbury Road, London W11 2AA
Tel. 0171-727 7915 Fax. 0171-792 9073
Member: British Antique Dealers' Association
Member: Society of London Art Dealers
Antiquities, Old Master and 20th-century
paintings and drawings, early portraits, medieval
and Renaissance sculpture.
STAND NO. 4
STAND TEL. 0171-499 6363 *Ext.* 7104
pages 84, 224 - 225

Antony Preston Antiques Ltd
The Square, Stow-on-the-Wold,
Cheltenham, Gloucestershire GL54 1AB
Tel. 01451-831586 Fax. 0171-581 5076
Member: British Antique Dealers' Association
Member: Cotswold Antique Dealers' Association
18th- and early 19th-century English furniture,
clocks and barometers.
STAND NO. 51
STAND TEL. 0171-499 6363 *Ext.* 7151
pages 146 - 147

Pyms Gallery
9 Mount Street, Mayfair,
London W1Y 5AD
Tel. 0171-629 2020 Fax. 0171-629 2060
Member: British Antique Dealers' Association
Member: Society of London Art Dealers
18th-, 19th- and 20th-century British and Irish
paintings and drawings, French 19th-century
paintings.
STAND NO. 46
STAND TEL. 0171-499 6363 *Ext.* 7146
pages 226 - 229

Brian Rolleston Ltd
104A Kensington Church Street,
London W8 4BU
Tel. and Fax. 0171-229 5892
Member: British Antique Dealers' Association
Furniture.
STAND NO. 72
STAND TEL. 0171-499 6363 *Ext.* 7172
pages 148 - 149

Alistair Sampson Antiques Ltd
120 Mount Street, London W1Y 5HB
Tel. 0171-409 1799 Fax. 0171-409 7717
Member: British Antique Dealers' Association
Oak furniture, brass, needlework, primitive paintings,
pottery, decorative and unusual items, treen.
STAND NO. 45
STAND TEL. 0171-499 6363 *Ext.* 7145
pages 42, 69, 185, 232

Seago
22 Pimlico Road, London SW1W 8LJ
Tel. 0171-730 7502 Fax. 0171-730 9179
Member: British Antique Dealers' Association
Garden sculpture and ornament.
STAND NO. 85
STAND TEL. 0171-499 6363 *Ext.* 7185
pages 86 - 87

Spink & Son Ltd
5 King Street, St James's, London SW1Y 6QS
Tel. 0171-930 7888 Fax. 0171-839 4853
Telex 916711
Member: British Antique Dealers' Association
Member: Society of London Art Dealers
English paintings and watercolours, jewellery, fine
English furniture, Chinese and Japanese ceramics
and works of art, Indian and South East Asian
sculpture, Islamic works of art, European and
Eastern textiles, coins, medals and decorations,
stamps, furniture restoration.
STAND NO. 1
STAND TEL. 0171-499 6363 *Ext.* 7101
pages 171 - 173, 230 - 231, 261

Stair & Company Ltd
14 Mount Street, London W1Y 5RA
Tel. 0171-499 1784 Fax. 0171-629 1050
and 942 Madison Avenue,
New York, N.Y. 10021, U.S.A.
Member: British Antique Dealers' Association
Member: Confédération Internationale des Négociants
en Œuvres d'Art
18th-century English furniture and works of art,
mirrors, chandeliers, clocks and barometers,
needlework and tapestry, lamps.
STAND NO. 66
STAND TEL. 0171-499 6363 *Ext.* 7166
pages 150 - 152

Stoppenbach & Delestre Ltd
25 Cork Street, London W1X 1HB
Tel. 0171-734 3534 Fax. 0171-494 3578
Member: Society of London Art Dealers
Member: Syndicat National des Antiquaires
19th- and 20th-century French paintings,
drawings, and sculpture.
STAND NO. 52
STAND TEL. 0171-499 6363 *Ext.* 7152
pages 233 - 235

Tadema Gallery
10 Charlton Place, Camden Passage,
London N1 8AJ
Tel.and Fax. 0171-359 1055
Member: British Antique Dealers' Association
Member: LAPADA - The Association of Art and
Antique Dealers
Jewellery and decorative arts from the late
19th- and 20th-centuries.
STAND NO. 21
STAND TEL. 0171-499 6363 *Ext.* 7121
pages 266 - 267

The Temple Gallery
6 Clarendon Cross, London W11 4AP
Tel. 0171-727 3809 Fax. 0171-727 1546
Byzantine and early Russian icons.
STAND NO. 37
STAND TEL. 0171-499 6363 *Ext.* 7137
page 85

Ursus Books & Prints
981 Madison Avenue, New York,
N.Y. 10021, U.S.A.
(Mezzanine of the Carlyle Hotel)
Tel. 212-772 8787 Fax. 212-737 9306
Member: Antiquarian Booksellers' Association of
America
Member: International League of Antiquarian
Booksellers
Rare books in all fields, art reference books,
decorative prints and watercolours.
STAND NO. 25
STAND TEL. 0171-499 6363 *Ext.* 7125
page 33

Rafael Valls Ltd
11 Duke Street, St James's,
London SW1Y 6BN
Tel. 0171-930 1144 Fax. 0171-976 1596
6 Ryder Street, St James's,
London SW1Y 6QB
Tel. 0171-930 0029 Fax. 0171-976 1596
Member: British Antique Dealers' Association
Member: Society of London Art Dealers
Old Masters, 18th- and 19th-century British and
European paintings.
STAND NO. 18
STAND TEL. 0171-499 6363 *Ext.* 7118
pages 236 - 237

Johnny Van Haeften Ltd
13 Duke Street, St James's,
London SW1Y 6DB
Tel. 0171-930 3062 Fax. 0171-839 6303
Member: British Antique Dealers' Association
Member: Society of London Art Dealers
16th- and 17th-century Dutch and Flemish Old
Master paintings.
STAND NO. 63
STAND TEL. 0171-499 6363 *Ext.* 7163
pages 238 - 240

Vanderven & Vanderven Oriental Art
Peperstraat 6, 5211 KM 's-Hertogenbosch,
The Netherlands
Tel. 31-73 61 46 251 Fax. 31-73 61 30 662
Oriental art.
STAND NO. 70
STAND TEL. 0171-499 6363 *Ext.* 7170
pages 174 - 175

Mark J. West - Cobb Antiques Ltd
39B High Street, Wimbledon Village,
London SW19 5EY
Tel. and Fax. 0181-946 2811
Member: British Antique Dealers' Association
18th- and 19th-century English and continental
glass.
STAND NO. 6
STAND TEL. 0171-499 6363 *Ext.* 7106
pages 70 - 71

William Weston Gallery
7 Royal Arcade, Albemarle Street,
London W1X 4JN
Tel. 0171-493 0722 Fax. 0171-491 9240
Member: Society of London Art Dealers
Member: Chambre Syndicale de l'Estampe et du
Dessin, Paris
Member: International Fine Print Dealers'
Association, New York
Modern graphic works by European and British
artists.
STAND NO. 27
STAND TEL. 0171-499 6363 *Ext.* 7127
page 241

O.F. Wilson Ltd
Queen's Elm Parade, Old Church Street,
London SW3 6EJ
Tel. 0171-352 9554 Fax. 0171-351 0765
Member: British Antique Dealers' Association
Member: LAPADA - The Association of Art and
Antique Dealers
English and Continental decorative furniture and
works of art, 1700-1860, period mantelpieces,
architectural items, drawings, prints and
engravings.
STAND NO. 7
STAND TEL. 0171-499 6363 *Ext.* 7107
pages 153 - 155

Witney Antiques
96-100 Corn Street, Witney,
Oxfordshire OX8 7BU
Tel. 01993 703902 Fax. 01993 779852
Member: British Antique Dealers' Association
English and Continental furniture, clocks,
needlework and works of art.
STAND NO. 50
STAND TEL. 0171-499 6363 *Ext.* 7150
pages 43, 156 - 157

Christopher Wood
20 Georgian House, 10 Bury Street,
London SW1Y 6AA
Tel. and Fax. 0171-839 3963
Member: Society of London Art Dealers
Member: British Antique Dealers' Association
Fine 19th-century paintings, watercolours and
drawings, 19th-century furniture and works of art.
STAND NO. 77
STAND TEL. 0171-499 6363 *Ext.* 7177
pages 242 - 245

Anthony Woodburn Ltd
Orchard House, High Street, Leigh,
Nr Tonbridge, Kent TN11 8RH
Tel. 01732-832258 Fax. 01732-838023
Member: British Antique Dealers' Association
Clocks and barometers.
STAND NO. 67
STAND TEL. 0171-499 6363 *Ext.* 7167
pages 52 - 53

Clifford Wright Antiques Ltd
104-106 Fulham Road, London SW3 6HS
Tel. 0171-589 0986 Fax. 0171-589 3565
Member: British Antique Dealers' Association
Furniture, period mirrors and works of art.
STAND NO. 76
STAND TEL. 0171-499 6363 *Ext.* 7176
pages 158 - 159

Grace Wu Bruce
701 Universal Trade Centre,
3 Arbuthnot Road, Hong Kong
Tel. 852-2537 1288 Fax. 852-2537 0213
Chinese furniture and works of art.
STAND NO. 41
STAND TEL. 0171-499 6363 *Ext.* 7141
pages 176 - 179

PLAN OF THE FAIR

	STAND NO.
A La Vieille Russie, Inc	65
Norman Adams Ltd	47
William Agnew	9
Luís Alegria	39
Apter-Fredericks Ltd	78
Aronson Antiquairs	61
Asprey	11
Avon Antiques	86
Joanna Barnes Fine Arts	3
H.C. Baxter & Sons	24
Michele Beiny, Inc	84
Konrad O. Bernheimer Ltd	62
H. Blairman & Sons Ltd	53
J.H. Bourdon-Smith Ltd	75
The British Antique Dealers' Association	2
John Carlton-Smith	55
Antoine Chenevière Fine Arts	54
Richard Courtney Ltd	32
Devenish	71
William Drummond	26
Andrew Edmunds	8

ENTRANCE FOYER AND
GREAT ROOM BALCONY
Exhibitor stands numbers 1-36

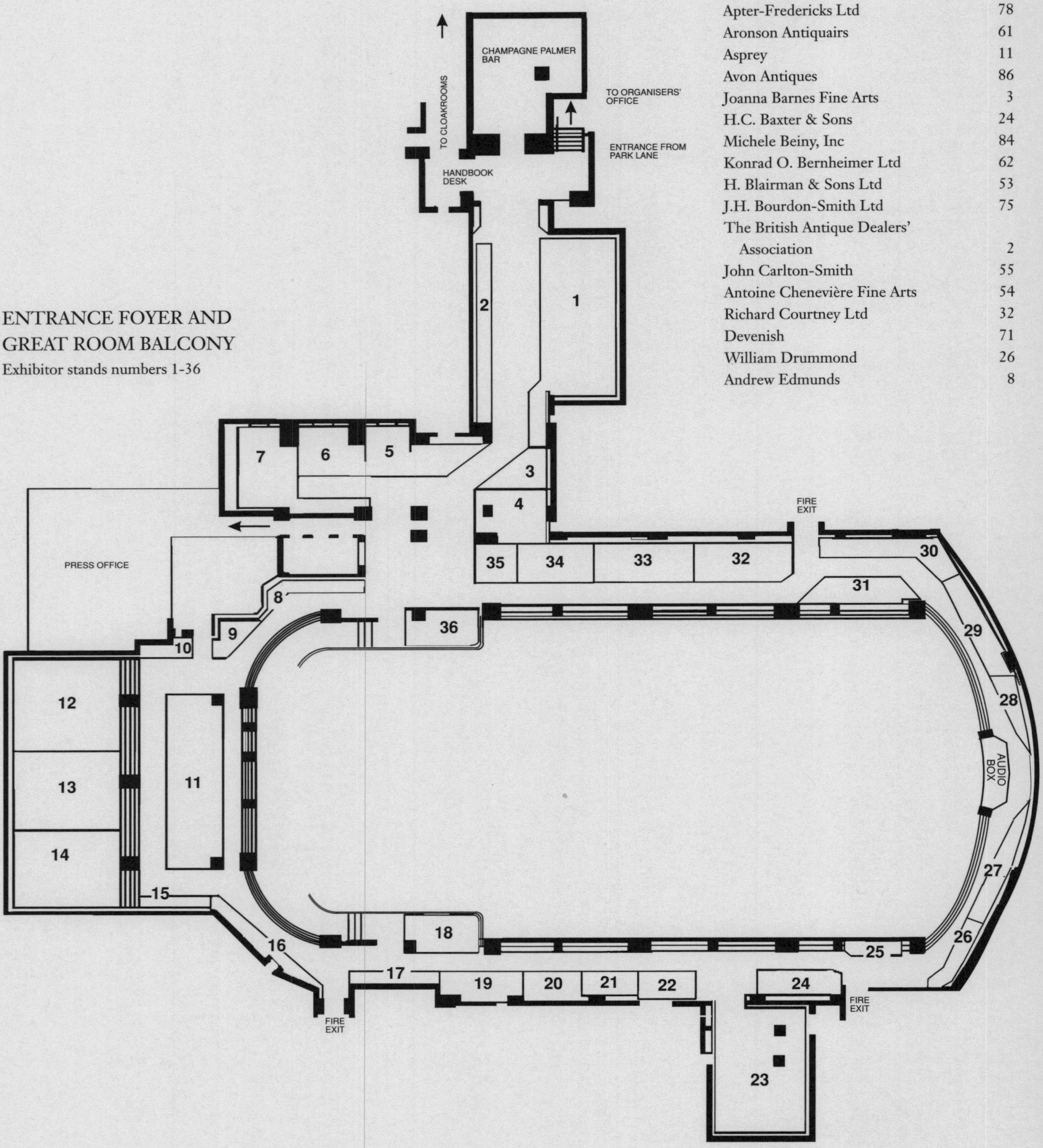

CHAMPAGNE PALMER BAR
TO CLOAKROOMS
TO ORGANISERS' OFFICE
ENTRANCE FROM PARK LANE
HANDBOOK DESK
PRESS OFFICE
FIRE EXIT
AUDIO BOX
FIRE EXIT
FIRE EXIT
1
2
3
4
5
6
7
8
9
10
11
12
13
14
15
16
17
18
19
20
21
22
23
24
25
26
27
28
29
30
31
32
33
34
35
36

	STAND NO.		STAND NO.		STAND NO.
Sam Fogg	49	D.S. Lavender (Antiques) Ltd	33	Antony Preston Antiques Ltd	51
A. & E. Foster	10	Michael Lipitch Ltd	14	Pyms Gallery	46
Michael Foster	40	Peter Lipitch Ltd	34	Brian Rolleston Ltd	72
Victor Franses Gallery	30	Mallett	12	Alistair Sampson Antiques Ltd	45
Gander & White Shipping Ltd	38	Mallett Gallery	5	Seago	85
Rupert Gentle Antiques	28	Mallett Glass	19	Spink & Son Ltd	1
Galerie Gismondi	57	S. Marchant & Son	43	Stair & Company Ltd	66
Michael Goedhuis	56	Mayorcas Ltd	44	Stoppenbach & Delestre Ltd	52
Richard Green	59	Duncan R. Miller Fine Arts	83	Tadema Gallery	21
Martyn Gregory	79	Peter Nahum at The Leicester		The Temple Gallery	37
Grosvenor Antiques Ltd	48	Galleries Ltd	81	Ursus Books & Prints	25
Halcyon Days	35	Galerie Neuse Kunsthandel	23	Rafael Valls Ltd	18
Robert Hall	20	Newhouse Galleries, Inc	68	Johnny Van Haeften Ltd	63
Hancocks & Company	31	Noortman	42	Vanderven & Vanderven Oriental Art	70
Jonathan Harris	69	The O'Shea Gallery	16	Mark J. West – Cobb Antiques Ltd	6
Thomas Heneage Art Books	15	Pelham Galleries Ltd	64	William Weston Gallery	27
Hotspur Ltd	60	Jacques et Patrick Perrin	73	O.F. Wilson Ltd	7
Iona Antiques	29	David Pettifer Ltd	58	Witney Antiques	50
Jeremy Ltd	74	Trevor Philip & Sons Ltd	36	Christopher Wood	77
C. John	80	Ronald Phillips Ltd	82	Anthony Woodburn Ltd	67
Klaber & Klaber	17	S.J. Phillips Ltd	13	Clifford Wright Antiques Ltd	76
David Koetser Gallery	22	Richard Philp	4	Grace Wu Bruce	41

GREAT ROOM
Exhibitor stands numbers 37-86

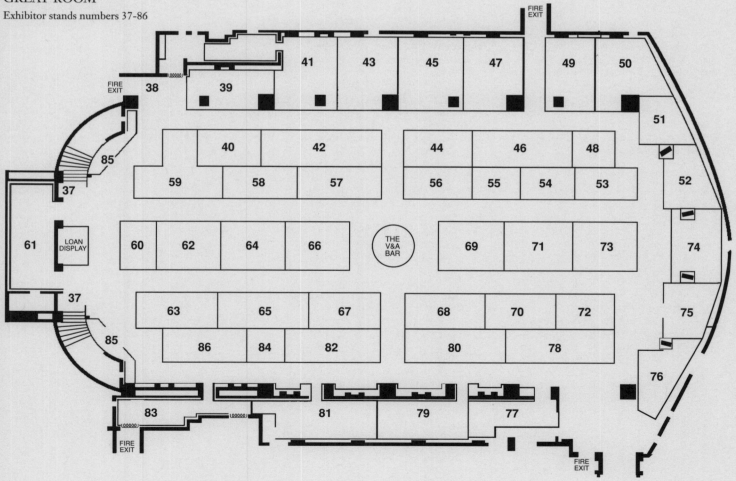

WHAT IS THE BADA?

The British Antique Dealers' Association is the leading association for the antiques trade. It was founded in 1918 by a group of sixteen dealers to lobby against a government proposal to introduce a luxury tax. As a result of this small pressure group, the proposal was dropped. Following this successful initiative the Association has grown and now represents some 400 of the country's foremost dealers.

These elected members have a wide variety of specialities ranging from architectural items to icons, from textiles and model ships to miniatures and manuscripts. The membership is widely spread throughout Britain, from Aberystwyth to East Anglia, from Edinburgh to south Devon, yet the greatest concentration remains in London. These 400 dealers provide Britain with the greatest resource of knowledge and expertise to be found in the world of antiques and fine art.

A Campaigning Association

Over the years, the BADA has continued its role as a campaigning organisation, and has fought to maintain a strong domestic market. One of the prime objectives of the Association has always been to ensure the most favourable conditions for the buying and selling of antiques, not only for dealers, but also for the benefit of collectors, both private and public.

In 1996, the BADA, with the other trade associations and the auction houses, was instrumental in forming The British Art Market Federation, which is dedicated to fighting adverse legislation emanating from the E.C. In 1918, the BADA was formed to fight unfavourable British legislation and it continues to campaign vigorously for the benefit of the British art market.

A recent directive from Brussels, harmonising VAT throughout the European Union, has endangered the strong position of London and the UK in the art market by imposing an import tax on goods from outside the Community. Free trade in works of art is essential to the maintenance of this country's position in the international market, against competition from other art trade centres, such as New York.

The BADA continues to represent the interests of the art world and preserve Britain's position, thereby ensuring the continued prosperity of the arts for everyone, whether they be collectors, restorers, agents, shippers or dealers.

A Professional Association

The staff of the Association's London headquarters at 20 Rutland Gate provide a wide range of consumer information and administer an arbitration service.

Long before the advent of the Trade Descriptions Act, members of the BADA adhered to a stringent code of practice which is overseen by the Council and officers of the Association. Any dispute between a member and his customer can be taken to the free arbitration service, which provides a rapid judgement at no cost to the consumer, by the same experts who would be likely to be called as expert witnesses in any legal action.

Membership of the Association is closely monitored. Before any proposed new member may be recommended to Council, at least four written reports are scrutinised by the Membership Committee. The Council must then approve the new member's application by at least a 75 per cent majority before the Cellini emblem may be displayed. Moreover, each member undergoes an annual confirmation of his membership, to ensure that any dealer

representing the Association maintains a high professional standard of business and expertise. It is for this reason that a member of the public can continue to buy from, and sell to, a member of the BADA with confidence.

A Caring Association

Another of the Association's prime objectives is to promote good relations between the antiques trade and the public, not only to preserve the present market but also to ensure its future. A good dealer is conscious that he is the custodian and preserver of the artworks which he handles for future generations.

To this end, the Association has established a Cultural and Educational Trust – a charity financed by the Association and its members, which supports a number of causes. It is linked very closely with West Dean College and offers bursaries to students who undertake the courses in restoration of ceramics, clocks, furniture and metalwork.

Many members give their time and expertise to help students by lecturing and examining particular aspects of various courses. Experienced restoration is of use not only to BADA members, but also to private collectors, museums, English Heritage and other public bodies. This charitable sponsorship ensures that much-valued skills are retained for the future.

Members of the BADA were instrumental in starting the first Antique Dealers' Fair at Grosvenor House in 1934 and the Association has continued this close involvement with Britain's premier fair at which so many of its members exhibit.

The British Antique Dealers' Association is proud to have organised the loan exhibition from the Victoria and Albert Museum at this year's Fair.

THE BRITISH ANTIQUE DEALERS' ASSOCIATION

For further information: The British Antique Dealers' Association, 20 Rutland Gate, London SW7 1BD.   Telephone: 0171-589 4128.   Fax: 0171-581 9083

LIST OF EXHIBITORS BY CATEGORY

BOOKS, MAPS AND MANUSCRIPTS

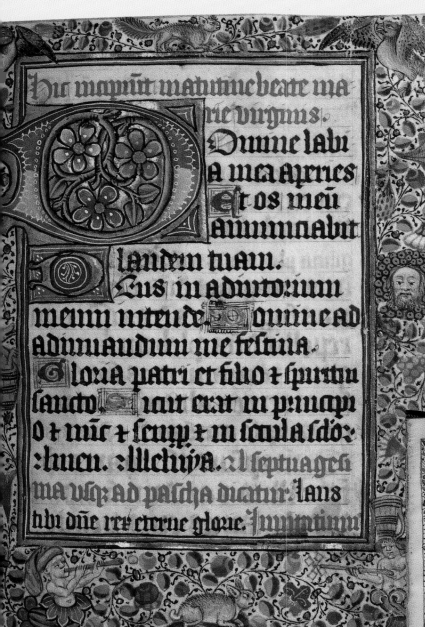

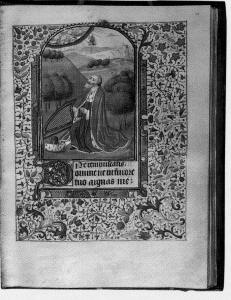

Detail from one of nearly 1300 German, hand-coloured rococo engravings, the majority by Martin Engelbrecht (1684-1756) of Augsburg.
Ursus Books & Prints

Detail from an opening of a Book of Hours made for the Roberts family of Essex, circa 1480.
Sam Fogg

King David, from a Book of Hours, Rouen, circa 1440, made during the occupation of the English.
Sam Fogg

Sam Fogg,
35 St George Street,
London W1R 9FA
Tel: 0171-495 2333
Fax: 0171-409 3326

The Bute Hours, an English Book of Hours with 53 large miniatures and 35 historiated initials, made for a nobleman of the Royal Household. London or Windsor, circa 1500. 22.8 x 15.9 cm (9 x 6 1/4 in).

This is a spectacular Book of Hours, written in Latin and English, with 53 large miniatures and more than 200 decorated initials. Although it seems to be the richest English Book of Hours to have survived from this time, the name of the owner is not known. There are some clues, however, which associate it closely with the Royal Household. The feast days listed include many of English Kings, and the open miniature shows the banner of St George. There are numerous paintings of the owner and his family, one of which shows the patron kneeling before King Henry VI. Although never canonised, Henry is depicted as a saint, and this may reveal a connection with St George's chapel, Windsor, where his cult was promoted.

Sam Fogg,
35 St George Street,
London W1R 9FA
Tel: 0171-495 2333
Fax: 0171-409 3326

A Latin bible from the Abbey of Tongerloo, written in Italy in the mid 13th century.
23.5 x 16.5 cm (9 ^{1}/$_4$ x 6 ^{1}/$_2$ in).

Manuscripts of the Bible, minutely written, are among the most characteristic and precious objects to survive from the 13th century. This large and complete example was made in Italy, probably near Genoa, some time in the 1250s or 1260s. It has three small miniatures and nearly 100 decorated initials, many with dragons and monsters. By the late Middle Ages, this Bible had become the property of the great Abbey of Tongerloo, near Brussels.

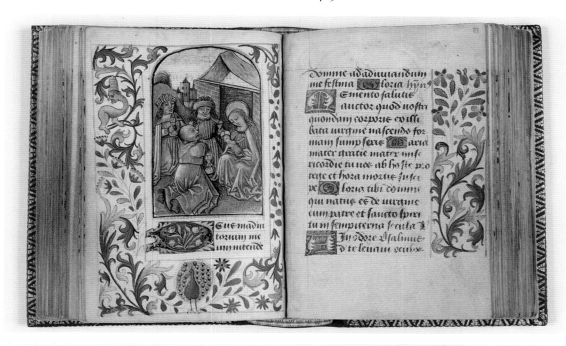

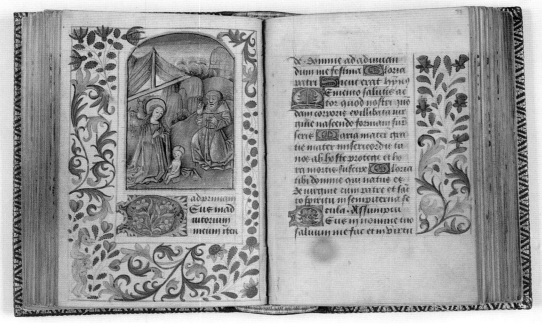

Sam Fogg,
35 St George Street,
London W1R 9FA
Tel: 0171-495 2333
Fax: 0171-409 3326

A Book of Hours, with 21 miniatures painted in *grisaille*. Tournai, 1460. 10.9 x 7.8 cm (4 ¼ x 3 in).

This small but very fine manuscript was probably made in Tournai in the southern Netherlands in the 1460s. It is one of a small number of manuscripts made there using a technique called *grisaille*. By restricting the colour of the figures to black and white, a delicate and refined atmospheric effect is achieved. The greys are countered with delicate touches of gold on the figures and with blue in the sky. The master of this technique was an artist named Jean Le Tavernier, who lived in Tournai, and decorated manuscripts for the Burgundian Court. This book must be a product of his workshop.

Thomas Heneage Art Books,
42 Duke Street,
St James's,
London SW1Y 6DJ
Tel 0171-930 9223
Fax: 0171-839 9223

A collection of 18th-century auction catalogues including the Gersaint sales (1736 - 1747) and various others. The fourteen Gersaint catalogues comprise three volumes, and are bound in 18th-century calf.
17 x 10.3 cm (6 ³/₄ x 4 in).
Literature: *Lugt. Répertoire des Catalogues des Ventes Publiques,* vol. I, 1600-1825, The Hague 1938.

Edmé-François Gersaint (1694-1750), the French *marchand-mercier,* picture dealer and publisher, was an intimate friend of François Watteau, whose works he published as prints. Two of the frontispieces of these catalogues are designed by Boucher, a third being by Cochin. By the early 1730s, Gersaint had expanded his business to include the sale of shells, lacquer, porcelain, and curiosities, which led to the production of catalogues. One of the earliest sales to be illustrated was the highly important collection including the jewels of Charles Godefroy (1736). The catalogue of Quentin de Lorangère (1744) contains biographies of Jacques Callot and Watteau.

    Other catalogues in this collection include those of La Live de Jully (1769), a patron of contemporary French painters

and a celebrated collector of furniture; Jean de Jullienne (1767), a textile manufacturer who left a wealth of French, Italian and Netherlandish masterpieces from Watteau to Bloemart and Titian; and Randon de Boisset (1777), who collected valuable 17th-century Dutch and 17th- and 18th- century French works, most notably by Boucher, as well as marble sculptures, porcelain, hardstone, lacquerware and Boulle furniture.

Ursus Books & Prints,
981 Madison Avenue,
(in the Carlyle Hotel),
New York,
N.Y. 10021
U.S.A.
Tel: 212-772 8787
Fax: 212-737 9306

The Royal Pavilion at Brighton by John Nash. London: Rudolph Ackermann, 1826.
Engraved title and list of plates, 31 aquatint plates, printed in colour and finished by hand. Folio, bound by Sangorski & Sutcliffe in three-quarter citron morocco, spine gilt, marbled endpapers.

This is a first edition, first issue, of a magnificent English Regency colour-plate book, and is richly and extensively hand-coloured. It is the most lavish record of the Brighton Pavilion ever published, and probably the most sumptuous record of any English building.

In 1820, George IV commissioned Nash to publish a deluxe guide to the Royal Pavilion at Brighton for his illustrious guests. Nash asked his pupil, Augustus Pugin, to do the illustrations, which he executed brilliantly in the form of aquatints, printed in colour and finished by hand. Brunet claimed that only 250 copies of this first issue were printed. This exceptionally fine, bright copy comes from the Furstenberg Collection.

CARPETS AND TEXTILES

An Indo-Portuguese embroidered coverlet from the city of Goa, circa 1720. C. John

A Charles II silk raised work and needlework picture depicting scenes from the life of Joseph. English, circa 1660. Witney Antiques

Detail of an English (or Northern French) needlework valance, circa 1580, Mayorcas Ltd

An English silk marriage purse embroidered with portraits of a young man and woman, circa 1660. Witney Antiques

C. John,
70 South Audley Street,
London W1Y 5FE
Tel: 0171-493 5288
Fax: 0171-409 7030

An Eastern European Bessarabian carpet, circa 1800. Wool on a woollen foundation. Length 409 cm (161 in). Width 371 cm (146 in).

This wonderful carpet was woven in the area bordering Romania and the Ukraine, known as Moldova or Bessarabia. The method of weaving is similar to that employed in the better-known kelim carpets, which produces a pile-less fabric that is often reversible.

Bessarabian carpet designs frequently reflect those of French Savonnerie and English needle-work carpets. Both these influences are evident in this particular carpet, which is of the finest quality. Highly decorative carpets of this kind are much sought after, and it is rare to find one so well preserved.

C. John,
70 South Audley Street,
London W1Y 5FE
Tel: 0171-493 5288
Fax: 0171-409 7030

A French Aubusson carpet, circa 1800, (1st Empire period). Wool on a cotton foundation. 479 x 387 cm (189 x 152 in).

In the final quarter of the 18th century, factories in the town of Aubusson expanded their production of wall tapestries to include flat-weave, or tapestry-woven, carpets. These were woven using the slit-tapestry method, which left small openings or slits that were later sewn together. This technique produced good definition of design and clarity of colour. Aubusson carpets proved to be so popular that today the name is widely applied to all European carpets without pile.

This exquisite example, of large proportions, is finely woven and has a design with a central medallion, typical of the period. It remains in a very good state of preservation, with only minor restorations.

M·R·D·AVBVSSON ·F·GRELLET

C. John,
70 South Audley Street,
London W1Y 5FE
Tel: 0171-493 5288
Fax: 0171-409 7030

A French Royal Aubusson 'verdure' tapestry, circa 1770. Signed, *Manufacture Royale D' Aubusson* , and by the master weaver, F. Grellet. Silk and wool on a linen foundation. 274 x 233 cm (110 x 88 in).

Tapestries depicting woodland scenes are known as 'verdure' tapestries. They have been fashionable and popular over the centuries in various forms, contributing an unobtrusive, calm atmosphere to a room setting. Factories in the towns of

Aubusson and Felletin produced many such tapestries in the latter part of the 18th century.

This very finely woven example remains in its original state, without any restoration or fading.

**Mayorcas Ltd.,
8 Duke Street,
St James's,
London SW1Y 6BN
Tel: 0171-839 3100
Fax: 0171-839 3223**

A superb Flemish (Enghien) 'game park' tapestry, circa 1580, depicting various wild animals in a lush rustic setting, edged with original borders of allegorical figures, urns filled with fruits, flowers, and rich foliage.
270 x 320 cm (106 ½ x 120 in).

The vogue for 'game park' or 'garden' tapestries developed in the middle of the 16th century, encouraged by the keen interest of the intelligentsia in zoology and topography. With their extensive foliage, vistas of rich, rural landscape and lively depictions of wildlife, these tapestries appealed to the aristocracy and nobility of the day. Around 1555 - 1565, King Sigismund Augustus I, King of Poland, was placing massive orders in Brussels for tapestries to furnish his castle at Wawel in Cracow. Among these were the 44 pieces known as 'Animals and Birds in Landscapes'.

Animals and birds figured strongly in landscape or 'game park' tapestries, the foreground being treated almost as a zoological portrait. Such zoological interest coincided with the publication of Conrad Gestner's *Historical Animalium* in Zurich in the 1550s.

The borders of the tapestry incorporate grotesque human figures caught in decorative metalwork *('ferronnerie')*, a style originally conceived by the Antwerp artist Cornelis Floris in 1548.

(Literature: Guy Delmarcel, *Tapisseries Anciennes d'Enghien*, p.46-47, pl.18. Heinrich Gobel, *Wandteppiche*, I, vol. 2, pl.162. G.F. Wingfield Digby, *The Tapestry Collection, Medieval and Renaissance*, HMSO 1980, p.58.)

Mayorcas Ltd.,
8 Duke Street,
St James's,
London SW1Y 6BN
Tel: 0171-839 3100
Fax: 0171-839 3223

An exquisite and colourful
English embroidered sampler by
'Margrett Clare, Aged Twelve',
dated 1734.
44.5 x 38 cm (17 ¹/₂ x 15 in).

Samplers are the most familiar of
all old embroideries. The word
itself derives from the old French
exemplaire or *essemplaire*, meaning
any kind of model or pattern to be
imitated or copied. The earliest
recorded reference is an item in
the Privy Purse expenses of
Queen Elizabeth of York in 1502,
'for an elne of lynnyn cloth for a
sampler for the Quene,
viij d'. In 1523, the poet John
Skelton mentioned the social

aspects of the textile crafts in
16th-century England, 'With that
the tappettis and carpets were layd
whereon theis ladys softly myght
rest, the sampler to sow on, the
lacis to embraid.'

Through the centuries, most
samplers have been worked by
girls between the ages of nine and
sixteen, with designs taken from
the pattern books available at the
time. Changes of fashion caused
the sampler to evolve from a

collection of simple patterns into a
sophisticated decorative object in
its own right, to be admired for its
intrinsic beauty as an embroidered
picture. The height of this
development was in 18th-century
England. The quality, colour and
condition of this sampler make it
an unparalleled example from this
period.

(Literature: Donald King,
Samplers, HMSO London 1960.)

Alistair Sampson Antiques Ltd.,
120 Mount Street,
London W1Y 5HB
Tel: 0171-409 1799
Fax: 0171-409 7717

An English needlework picture of Venus and Adonis with Cupid by a carp pond, surrounded by flowering trees, birds and dogs. Third quarter of the 17th century. Signed with initials 'AC'.
25 x 25 cm (9 ³/₄ x 9 ³/₄ in).

This picture is some way from the sobriety of much Stuart needlework, which is typified by images of the Sacrifice of Isaac, Ahasuerus with Esther, or a demure couple surrounded by subjects from the pattern book. Perhaps the needleworker at first mistook the picture for Joseph with Potiphar's wife, but humour must have prevailed over strict propriety (and unfamiliarity with life-drawing) to include the sun looking on with glee at the amorous antics below. Venus and Adonis, watched by Cupid, disport themselves against a skilfully arranged group of emblems of love, making this a most delightful subject.

Witney Antiques,
96-100 Corn Street,
Witney,
Oxfordshire
OX8 7BU
Tel: 01993-703902
Fax: 01993-779852

A rare band sampler embroidered by 'ANN HOLEWIL', dated 1699. English. Length 36 cm (14 in). Width 15cm (6 in).

This exceptional and recently discovered sampler is from an important group of samplers embroidered under the supervision of Judith Hayle. Edwina Ehrman of the Museum of London has traced the origins of the ten known samplers in this group to an area in Suffolk where Judith Hayle ('I.H.') probably ran a boarding school. The group comprises the following examples:
   1691 Hannah Canting
   (Fitzwilliam Museum)
   1691 Elizabeth Meadow
   (Museum of London)
   1693 Sarah Bantoft
   (Fitzwilliam Museum)
   1694 Mary Canting
   (Fitzwilliam Museum)
   1699 Ann Holewil

(the present example)
   1700 Prisca Phillips
   (Fitzwilliam Museum)
   1701 Elizabeth Burton
   (Philadelphia Museum of Art)
   1701 Elizabeth Scarles (illus.
   M. Jourdain, *Secular Embroidery*)
   1709 Mary Moyse
   (Fitzwilliam Museum)
   1710 Elizabeth Goodday
   (Dr Douglas Goodhart)

   The verse embroidered on this sampler is common to most of the group,
   'LOOK WELL TO / WHAT YOU TAKE IN HAND FOR / LARNING IS BETTER THAN HOUSE / OR LAND WHEN LAND IS GONE / AND MONEY SPENT THEN / LARNING IS MOST EXCELLENT'

   This sampler is most closely related in style to those by Elizabeth Burton, Elizabeth Scarles, Mary Moyes and Elizabeth Goodday, being worked in brightly coloured silks with very complex stitches and many identical motifs.

   An analysis of the dyes used for the threads in this sampler reveals that the principal colouring agents are cochineal, tannin, luteolin (probably from weld), and alizarin.

CLOCKS, WATCHES AND SCIENTIFIC INSTRUMENTS

An 18th-century silver and gilt automaton musical table clock by James Cox, circa 1760.
John Carlton-Smith

A French Louis XVI mantel clock, the case in the manner of Luc-Philippe Thomire, circa 1785.
Jeremy Ltd

Charles II silver-mounted ande sonnerie striking ring table clock by homas Tompion, London, ca 1680.
nthony Woodburn Ltd

A Charles II quarter-repeating month-duration walnut longcase clock by Thomas Tompion, London, No 64, circa 1682.
Anthony Woodburn Ltd

A mid 18th-century French armillary sphere.
Trevor Philip & Sons Ltd

**John Carlton-Smith,
17 Ryder Street,
St James's,
London SW1Y 6PY
Tel: 0171-930 6622
Fax: 0171-930 9719**

An outstanding George I walnut and gilt-brass mounted quarter-chiming bracket clock with three subsidiary dials for calendar, regulation and strike/silent.
Circa 1720.
Height 57 cm (22 in).

The maker, James Reith, was apprenticed in 1698 and was a member of the Clockmakers' Company from 1705-1736. He worked in London at the Strand.

**John Carlton-Smith,
17 Ryder Street,
St James's,
London SW1Y 6PY
Tel: 0171-930 6622
Fax: 0171-930 9719**

An extremely rare and elegant George III mahogany longcase clock of typical form by Thomas Mudge and William Dutton. The enamel dials are set within fine brass mouldings and superb gilt spandrels. Circa 1770.
Height 225 cm (88 in).

Thomas Mudge and William Dutton were apprenticed to George Graham and became among the most important and respected makers of the 18th century.

Asprey,
165-169 New Bond Street,
London W1Y 0AR
Tel: 0171-493 6767
Fax: 0171-491 0384

A noble George III gilt-metal mounted ebonised musical clock, signed, 'R.to Y. PEDRO HIGGS Y. DIEGO EVANS JUNTO. A LA BOLSA REAL de LONDRES'. Circa 1780. Height 86 cm (34 in).

The movement, with anchor escapement, is of eight day duration. The arched dial plate is pierced and decorated with white enamel chapters including two subsidiary dials; the white enamel tablet in the arch is inscribed with twelve tunes which play on 16 bells. There is also a central slow/fast regulation dial.

The inscription indicates that the clock was intended for the Spanish market. It translates to read, 'Robert and Peter Higgs and James Evans together at London's Royal Exchange'. These makers were in partnership from about 1780 at 7 Sweeting's Alley (Royal Exchange).

Galerie Neuse Kunsthandel,
Contrescarpe 14,
28203 Bremen,
Germany
Tel: 49-421 32 56 42
Fax: 49-421 32 86 11

A fine German Renaissance automaton clock in the form of a ship, the case of gilt-bronze and copper, the movement with iron plates. South German, end of the 16th century.
Height 71 cm (28 in).
Literature: Klaus Maurice, *Die deutsche Räderuhr*, vol. 2, Munich 1976, no. 296.
Exhibited: 'The Clockwork Universe, German Clocks and Automata 1550-1650', Bayerisches Nationalmuseum, Munich 1980 and Smithsonian Institution, Washington D.C., no. 71.

When the clock strikes, a separate train in the ship's hold moves a guard of Turks around the ship's mast.

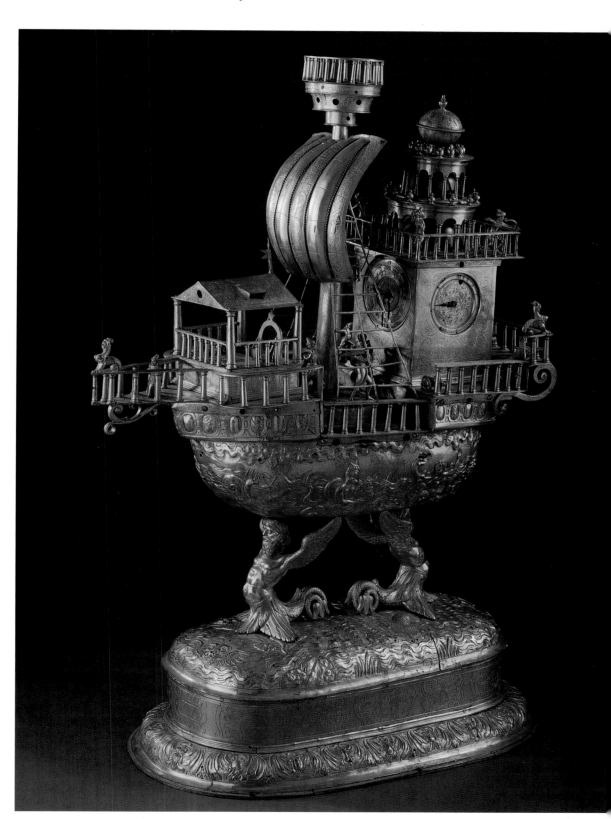

Trevor Philip & Sons Ltd.,
75A Jermyn Street,
St James's,
London SW1Y 6NP
Tel: 0171-930 2954
Fax: 0171-321 0212

A 19th-century mechanical orrery (or planetary system), circa 1850. Signed above the brass gear-work, 'Newton & Company, Opticians to the Queen, 3 Fleet Street, London' and further signed on the printed star plate, 'Newton & Son, 66 Chancery Lane, London'. Diameter of base plate 44.5 cm (17 ½ in).

The orrery has a wooden base plate with printed horizon papers incorporating the zodiac, a calendar scale, the various constellations of the zodiac, compass points and a degree scale. The geared mechanism allows all the planets to rotate around the gilded sun globe. Below the earth globe and moon, there is a silver disk engraved with the phases of the moon's orbit. The orrery is supported on three turned, wooden legs.

The most expensive part of an orrery or globe was the engraving, and the production of the printed papers used in its manufacture. Whereas the information on terrestrial globes needed frequent updating to keep abreast of the new discoveries by explorers, the heavens did not change, so the papers for celestial globes and orreries remained up to date and could be used well after their original production. This is why two different addresses appear on the present piece, Newton having moved from Chancery Lane to Fleet Street since the star plate was printed.

Trevor Philip & Sons Ltd.,
75A Jermyn Street,
St James's,
London SW1Y 6NP
Tel: 0171-930 2954
Fax: 0171-321 0212

A 17th-century gilt-brass astronomical compendium by Anthony Sneewins. Signed and dated, 'ANTHONY SNEEWINS 3/28 1666', (28 March 1666). The brass-mounted wooden case has a leather lining, and there is an outer case of soft leather. Base 9.3 cm square (3 ⁵/₈ in).

The back of the square base plate is engraved with a circular perpetual calendar, with town names and latitudes in the corners, and the words, '*CALENDARIUM.ET. NOVM.STYLVM.BY.ANTHONY. SNEEWINS.DELFT*'. The upper face is engraved in the four corners with the names of twelve European towns and their latitudes, and has in the centre a magnetic compass with compass rose. Around the compass rose is a horizontal dial with a hinged gnomon, fixed for 54 degrees. Mounted at the side is an equinoctial dial with a gnomon parallel to the polar axis. The cover to the compass is a nocturnal with carrying ring, engraved with degrees, months, declination, hours, and wind directions, over which moves an alidade with sights; more towns and latitudes are inscribed, from the centre, with winds and various North Sea locations, a lunar volvelle and aspectarium, and a table of epacts, with the date, 1666.

Anthony Woodburn Ltd.,
Orchard House,
High Street,
Leigh,
Kent TN11 8RH
Tel: 01732-832258
Fax: 01732-838023

A Charles II longcase clock of small and elegant proportions, veneered with walnut. Joseph Knibb, London, circa 1685. Height 200 cm (79 in).

This case is particularly small and elegantly proportioned, and has a rise-up hood. The movement has a duration of eight days, and the dial is ten inches square.

Joseph Knibb was one of the most eminent and influential clockmakers of the 17th century. He worked in Oxford prior to moving to London around 1670. In 1697, he returned to Hanslope, where he remained until his death in 1699. Literature: R.A. Lee, *The Knibb Family Clockmakers*, 1964, p. 35-47, 176; pl. 29 and 46.

Anthony Woodburn Ltd.,
Orchard House,
High Street,
Leigh,
Kent TN11 8RH
Tel: 01732-832258
Fax: 01732-838023

A rare and small Charles II ebony-veneered quarter-repeating spring table clock by Thomas Tompion, signed and numbered No. 99. London, circa 1683. Height 32 cm (12 ½ in). Provenance: Made by Tompion for the son of Sir Thomas Herbert. Sir Thomas walked to the scaffold in Whitehall with Charles I.

The two train movement has a verge escapement and is of such a size that it totally fills the case. The movement is fully latched and includes Tompion's complex Z-bar quarter-repeating mechanism, operated from either side of the case. The backplate is beautifully engraved with sprays of tulips and foliage, and is signed and numbered by the maker. The number is repeated on the case.

Thomas Tompion is regarded as the greatest English clockmaker. Through his association with Dr Robert Hooke, the Royal Society Curator of Experiments, he attracted the attention of Charles II. His elegantly designed cases, together with his complex and innovative mechanisms, set him apart from his contemporaries, and he was rewarded with royal patronage.

EUROPEAN CERAMICS
AND GLASS

*One of a pair of Regency
cut-glass and ormolu two-light
table lustres by John Blades of
London, circa 1820.
Mallett Glass*

*...ail of a polychrome Dutch
...ftware plaque shaped as a
...oda and decorated with
...nese figures, circa 1760.
...nson Antiquairs*

*A Meissen cockatoo modelled
by J.J. Kaendler, circa 1740.
Michele Beiny, Inc*

*A Minton vase, circa 1830.
Grosvenor Antiques Ltd*

Aronson Antiquairs,
Nieuwe Spiegelstraat 39,
1017 DC Amsterdam,
The Netherlands
Tel: 31-20 638 3103
Fax: 31-20 638 3066

An extremely rare blue and white Dutch Delftware bottle, decorated in great detail with birds and flowers after a Chinese example. Marked 'RIHS' for Rochus Jacobsz. Hoppesteyn, co-owner of 'Het Jong Moriaenshooft', (the Young Moor's Head) factory between 1679 and 1692. Last quarter of the 17th century, circa 1685. Height 15.5 cm (6 in).

Jacob Wemmersz. and his son, Rochus Jacobsz. Hoppesteyn, must be counted amongst the best faience manufacturers in Delft. They introduced poly-chrome decoration to Delft, using a process known as the mixed-technique, which involved firing polychrome objects first at a high temperature *(grand-feu)* for the basic colours like blue, and then again at a lower temperature *(petit-feu)* for other colours like red. Of the same high standard as the pieces in mixed-technique, signed by the master of the factory, are those made in blue and white.

The factory probably derived its name from the brewery that had previously occu-pied the building.

Aronson Antiquairs,
Nieuwe Spiegelstraat 39,
1017 DC Amsterdam,
The Netherlands
Tel: 31-20 638 3103
Fax: 31-20 638 3066

An extremely rare, large black Delftware tea-caddy and cover, decorated with Chinese land-scapes in yellow and green on a black ground, emulating Oriental lacquer decorated with gold. First quarter of the 18th century, circa 1705.
Height 14 cm (5 ½ in).

Black Delftware is regarded as the finest product of the Delft faience industry. Black was the most difficult colour to produce since the kiln temperature had to be exact. Black Delftware objects were therefore extremely rare and expensive. Only a few such objects are known in the world today, most of which are in the Evenepoel collection in the Musée Royaux d'Art et d'Histoire in Brussels, Belgium.

This type of tea-caddy, usually no taller than 10 centimetres, is always rectangular in shape. The cover closes with a screw thread. A tea-caddy with similar decoration, in the Victoria and Albert Museum in London, is marked 'LVE', for Lambertus van Eenhoorn, owner of 'De Metalen Pot' factory between 1691 and 1724.

Aronson Antiquairs,
Nieuwe Spiegelstraat 39,
1017 DC Amsterdam,
The Netherlands
Tel: 31-20 638 3103
Fax: 31-20 638 3066

A very rare polychrome Dutch Delftware circular box and cover, with elegant floral decoration executed with great delicacy in four colours – yellow, red, manganese-purple, and blue. Mid 18th-century, circa 1750. Height 12 cm (4 ³/₄ in).

Literature: Henry-Pierre Fourest, *Delftware, Faience production at Delft*, Thames & Hudson, London, 1980, pl. 155, p. 157.

The knob on the cover is in the form of a kneeling Chinaman,

which lends a special charm to the whole object. The purpose of this type of circular box is not certain, but they are usually called either comfit or tobacco boxes.

Aronson Antiquairs,
Nieuwe Spiegelstraat 39,
1017 DC Amsterdam,
The Netherlands
Tel: 31-20 638 3103
Fax: 31-20 638 3066

An extremely rare polychrome Dutch Delftware rectangular plaque decorated with a landscape, by Gijsbrecht Cleasz. Verhaast. Second quarter of the 18th century, circa 1730. 22.5 x 20 cm (8 ⅞ x 7 ⅞ in).

It was always assumed that the plaques decorated by Verhaast were made in the last quarter of the 17th century, since the only mention of him is in 1689 as a dish-maker at 'Het Jonge Moriaenshooft' (the Young Moor's Head) factory. This is probably where he acquired the technical knowledge of faience painting. After studying this plaque and several others in the Evenepoel collection in the Musée Royale d'Art et d'Histoire in Brussels, Belgium, we strongly believe that the few known plaques date from the first half of the 18th century.

The technique used is among the strangest at Delft during this period, imitating the appearance of oil paintings. There is also a striking similarity to the way glass-painters handled colours.

Michele Beiny, Inc.,
53 East 82nd Street,
New York,
N.Y. 10028, U.S.A.
Tel: 212-794 9357
Fax: 212-772 0119
London:
Tel: 0171-723 0456
Fax: 0171-723 4960
(By appointment only)

A superb pair of Meissen porcelain *Commedia dell'Arte* figures mounted on Louis XV ormolu two-light candelabra, with Vincennes flowers. The figures modelled by Johann Joachim Kaendler and Peter Reinicke, circa 1743 - 1744; the ormolu circa 1745 - 1749, stamped with crowned 'C's.
Height overall 24 cm (9 1/4 in).
Literature: H.E. Backer, *Komodienfiguren in der Sammlung Dr Ernst Schneider*, Keramik Freunde der Schweiz no. 50, p. 59-66; Erika Pauls-Eisenbeiss, *German Porcelain of the 18th Century*, vol. I, p. 319-341; Hugo Morley-Fletcher, *Meissen Porcelain*, p.85; Len & Yvonne Adams, *Meissen Portrait Figures*, p. 213-4.

These figures represent Pulchinella and Scaramouche from a series of about twenty *Commedia dell'Arte* figures created in 1743-1744 by Meissen's *Modellmeister* Kaendler, in collaboration with the recently employed Peter Reinicke, for Johann Adolph II, Duke of Saxe Weissenfels, first cousin of Augustus III of Saxony. They were probably made on the occasion of his second marriage to a princess of the House of Coburg-Gotha. The figures were derived from Joullain's and Callot's engravings for Louis Riccoboni's *Histoire du Theatre Italian*, published in Paris in 1727. Although the Italian Comedy was already a theme beloved of Meissen, the Weissenfels set was the first to cover the whole gamut of figures in one series. It was also the first substantial instance of porcelain figures derived from engraved sources. The crowned 'C's mark that appears on the ormolu was used between 1745 and 1749, introduced by a Royal Edict which ordered the striking of French bronzes with this mark to show that duty had been paid.

Michele Beiny, Inc.,
53 East 82nd Street,
New York,
N.Y. 10028, U.S.A.
Tel: 212-794 9357
Fax: 212-772 0119
London:
Tel: 0171-723 0456
Fax: 0171-723 4960
(By appointment only)

A superb pair of Sèvres ice-pails, covers and liners (*seaux à glace*) from a dessert service, decorated on a pale turquoise-blue *pointille* ground with baskets of flowers and trophies. Soft paste porcelain, marked with interlaced 'L's in blue, circa 1770- 1771.
Height 21.5 cm (8 ¼ in).
Provenance: The Earl of Sefton, Croxteth Hall; Eleanor Dorrance Ingersoll; President and Mrs Ferdinand Marcos.
Literature: for the shape, see Sir Geoffrey de Bellaigue, *Sèvres Porcelain in the Collection of Her Majesty the Queen: The Louis XVI Service*, pl. XX.

This service, known as The Sefton Service, comprises 48 pieces: two ice pails, two oval wine bottle coolers with dividers, two sugar tureens, four square compotiers, four circular compotiers, two oval compotiers, and 30 plates. The pale blue ground, interrupted by a *pointille* pattern of small white circles, was a speciality of Vincent Taillandier and his wife Genevieve, who applied this technique during the 1770s on a variety of wares using pale blue, green and pink grounds: it is often called *fond taillandier*. Of three services known to have been made with this turquoise *pointille* ground, one sold to the 1st Viscount Melbourne on 20 March 1771 (Firle Place, Sussex), another to Madame du Barry (Louis XV's mistress) in 1770. The former is decorated with putti on the shaped pieces and trophies on the others, the latter with putti throughout. The third service is the present one. In the absence of decorators' marks, the quality and style of the decoration suggest that the flowers may be by Noel, Levé, and J.B. Tandart, while the trophies are possibly the work of Charles Buteux, Chulot, and Morin.

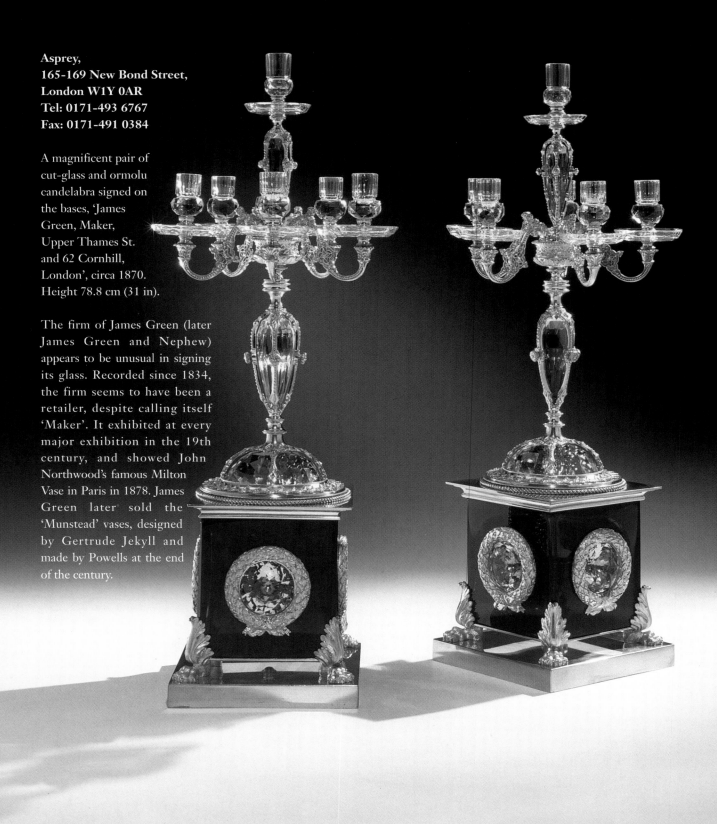

Asprey,
165-169 New Bond Street,
London W1Y 0AR
Tel: 0171-493 6767
Fax: 0171-491 0384

A magnificent pair of cut-glass and ormolu candelabra signed on the bases, 'James Green, Maker, Upper Thames St. and 62 Cornhill, London', circa 1870. Height 78.8 cm (31 in).

The firm of James Green (later James Green and Nephew) appears to be unusual in signing its glass. Recorded since 1834, the firm seems to have been a retailer, despite calling itself 'Maker'. It exhibited at every major exhibition in the 19th century, and showed John Northwood's famous Milton Vase in Paris in 1878. James Green later sold the 'Munstead' vases, designed by Gertrude Jekyll and made by Powells at the end of the century.

Jonathan Harris,
9 Lower Addison Gardens,
London W14 8BG
Tel: 0171-602 6255
Fax: 0171-602 0488

A rare faience corner *garde-robe* or close-stool, brilliantly decorated with the rich colours of the *grand-feu* on a luminous tin-glaze ground. The right side has an 18th-century replacement sliding wood panel, allowing removal of a cylindrical two-handled pot. Painted by, or by a hand close to, Pierre Chapelle, Rouen. Circa 1735.
Height 44.5 cm (17 1/2 in).
Width 55 cm (21 1/2 in).

Four related examples are known. One, very similar, is in the Musée du Louvre, (*Legs* Giraudeau, 1895/Inv. OA 3829). The Musée des Beaux-Arts, Rouen, has another, though with flattened bun feet; its condition does not allow public display. The museum also possesses a circular example, less grand in scale, and more modestly painted. The Museé National de la Céramique à Sèvres has a square *garde-robe*, similarly decorated and with the same feet as the present and the Louvre examples. Another, with these same feet, but of a lobed round form, was on the Paris art market in 1986.

This quality of faience replaced the silver services melted during the reign of Louis XIV

and, indeed, the factory persevered with shapes founded in Louis XIV silver into the second quarter of the century. Such an object as this could only be made in metal, wood or faience. Later in the century, the close stool went out of fashion, being replaced by *chaises percées* and chamber pots of silver, or of oriental or European porcelain. At Hampton Court and Knole, the surviving close stools, the grandest, are in wood, covered in costly velvet and silk. The earliest silver chamber pot recorded is of 1575, belonging to Queen Elizabeth, and the earliest thought to be extant, of 1670, was once part of the York Corporation plate. A gold one was pawned in 1672.

**Klaber & Klaber,
P.O. Box 9445,
London NW3 1WD
Tel: 0171-435 6537
Fax: 0171-435 9459**

An important early Derby group of Harlequin, Columbine and their baby, from the *Commedia dell'Arte* or the Italian Comedy. Circa 1756.
Height 21.75 cm (8 ¹/₂ in).
Literature: See Franklin A. Barrett & Arthur L. Thorpe, *Derby Porcelain 1750-1848*, 1971, cover and frontispiece, for an example from the Fitzwilliam Museum, Cambridge.

This soft-paste porcelain group is enamelled in colours typical of a Derby palette. Harlequin's suit is decorated with playing cards, and a rear panel of his jacket is painted with a bag spilling coins, a grotesque profile, and a satyr's face, all in puce.

The *Commedia dell'Arte* was a popular series of playlets performed by travelling troupes in Italy from the 16th century. The colourful protagonists of these plays were depicted by many artists, including Claude Gillot and Antoine Watteau, whose Italian Comedy paintings are well known. The engraver Joullain adapted Giacomo Carlotto's etchings of these characters to illustrate *Histoire du Théâtre Italien...* by Luigi Riccoboni. These engravings inspired modellers of the ceramic factories of Europe to produce sculptures in porcelain on this theme. Johann Joachim Kaendler, *Modellmeister* at the Meissen factory from 1733

until his death in 1775, created many different Italian Comedy figures. This Derby Italian Comedy group is an example of an English porcelain group that is directly inspired by Kaendler's Harlequin Family, modelled in 1740 (illustrated in L. & Y. Adams, *Meissen Portrait Figures*, 1987, p.204). In 1756, the Derby factory proclaimed that they were producing 'after the finest Dresden models', 'the nearest to Dresden', and that they were the 'second Dresden'. (Franklin & Barrett. p.19.)

Mallett,
Bourdon House,
2 Davies Street,
London W1Y 1LJ
Tel: 0171-629 2444
Fax: 0171-499 2670

An exceptional pair of late 18th-century Viennese porcelain fruit coolers, decorated with *grisaille* panels inspired by Antique sculpture. The bases are inscribed with the incised mark for 1794. Austrian, circa 1794. Height 44 cm (17 ¹/₂ in). Diameter (max) 81 cm (8 ¹/₄ in).

A factory making hard-paste porcelain was established in Vienna in 1719. It made baroque porcelain and exceptional figures. In 1784, under the control of Konrad von Sorgenthal, it created highly wrought tablewares, such as the pair of fruit coolers illustrated here. Sorgenthal became director of the Vienna porcelain manufactory in 1784, and remained there until his death in 1805. The era of his directorship remains the factory's finest, and its reputation continues today. He was responsible for the simple classical forms adopted for table wares. He introduced motifs derived from recent excavations in Pompeii, in particular the use of *grisaille* figures contained within fielded panels, as in the frescoes found there. However, his chief innovation was the use of intricate relief gilding which can be seen on the fruit coolers. This became a signature technique for the factory; its combination of delicacy with complexity has never been matched.

Mallett Glass,
141 New Bond Street,
London W1Y 0BS
Tel: 0171-499 7411
Fax: 0171-495 3179

A large diamond-point engraved roemer engraved *'Dit is Stomachael'*. The Netherlands, circa 1670.
Height 22.9 cm (9 in).
Provenance: collection A. J. Guépin; collection Joseph Ritman. Exhibited: Kunshalle, Dusseldorf, 1968, no. 112; Prinsenhof, Delft, 1969, no. 68.

This green tinted glass is engraved by a good hand. The inscription may be translated as 'Good for the digestion'.

Mallett Glass,
141 New Bond Street,
London W1Y 0BS
Tel: 0171-499 7411
Fax: 0171-495 3179

A Paris Exhibition engraved glass decanter and stopper with carafe en suite, each piece of ovoid form with wrythen moulded neck and trefoil rim. The body is engraved with ribbon-tied garlands of flowers, the neck with Greek key pattern, and the base with Vitruvian scrolls. Baccarat, Paris, circa 1878. Height of decanter 29 cm (11 ½ in). Provenance: Archives de la Manufacture de Baccarat.

This pattern is known as Service A, which was made exclusively for the Paris 'Exposition Universelle' in 1878. As far as is known, this pattern was not made for commercial production.

Jacques Perrin,
98 rue du Faubourg Saint-
Honoré,
75008 Paris,
France
Tel: 33-1 42 65 01 38
Fax: 33-1 49 24 04 08
and
Patrick Perrin,
178 rue du Faubourg Saint-
Honoré,
75008 Paris,
France
Tel: 33-1 40 76 07 76
Fax: 33-1 40 76 09 37

A Louis XV ormolu mantel clock
with Meissen porcelain figures
and flowers. Dial signed,
'GILLES L'AINE A PARIS'.
Porcelain signed under the base,
'Kaendler', for J.J. Kaendler,
received as *Modellmeister* in 1733.
Height 54 cm (21 ¼ in).
Width 35 cm (13 ¾ in).
Provenance: William S. Paley
Collection.

Alistair Sampson Antiques Ltd.,
120 Mount Street,
London W1Y 5HB
Tel: 0171-409 1799
Fax: 0171-409 7717

An outstanding example of the work of Pountney and Co, inscribed 'Bristol Pottery 1820' in red manuscript on the base. Height 56 cm (22 in).

The cistern and cover are decorated with a running border of leaves and hazelnuts, beneath which are painted three birds, each named on the base: 'The Brown Indian Dove', 'The South American Redstart', and 'The American Nightingale'.

The Bristol City Museum and Art Gallery possesses a somewhat similar cistern (52 cm high) which is inscribed 'Bristol Pottery 1814', and painted with naturalistic flowers. It was purchased in 1906 for £13.00.

Mark J. West,
Cobb Antiques Ltd.,
39b High Street,
Wimbledon Village,
London SW19 5EY
Tel. and Fax: 0181-946 2811

Two extremely rare mid 19th-century champagne glasses made in the Venetian style, with ser-pentine stems enclosing red, white, and blue coloured glass canes, the cup-shaped bowls hand-engraved with vine leaves and garlands.
Height 15 cm (6 in).

These glasses were made by the Birmingham firm of George Bacchus for 'The Great Exhibition of Works of Industry of all Nations', held in Joseph Paxton's Crystal Palace in Hyde Park, London, and opened by Queen Victoria and Prince Albert on 1 May 1851. One other glass of this design is known and is in the collection of the Victoria and Albert Museum.

Inset is a page from the official catalogue of the Great Exhibition showing an illustration of these glasses. Documentary pieces from this exhibition have a special significance, since the Great Exhibition marked the change from Georgian to Victorian design.

Mark J. West,
Cobb Antiques Ltd.,
39b High Street,
Wimbledon Village,
London SW19 5EY
Tel. and Fax: 0181-946 2811

Three crystal decanters, two of mallet form, the other of a shape known as 'Indian club', each engraved with a label, respectively 'Port', 'Claret', and 'White Wine'.
Circa 1770 - 1780.
Height 30 cm (11 ¾ in).

These decanters come from a rare group made around 1770-1780, characterised by their engraved labels which give an idea of the types of drink popular at this time.

European Sculpture and Works of Art

(Including Ormolu, Antiquities, Icons and Glass Pictures)

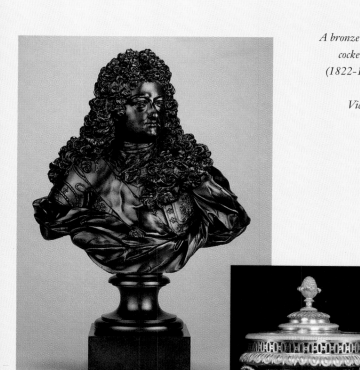

A bronze model of a standing cockerel by Auguste Cain (1822-1894), inscribed and dated 1880.
Victor Franses Gallery

A bronze bust of Philippe D'Orléans (1674-1723), Regent of France (1715-23), by Jean-Louis Lemoyne (1665-1755), inscribed and dated 1720.
Jonathan Harris

One of a pair of late 18th-century blue john and ormolu perfume burners, circa 1790.
Ronald Phillips Ltd.

...tail of Diana the ...ntress, a life-sized ...rble statue by William ...eed the Younger, signed ...d dated 1837.
...go

The Age of Innocence by Alfred Drury (1859-1944), bronze, signed and dated 1909.
William Agnew

William Agnew,
58 Englefield Road,
London N1 4HA
Tel. and Fax: 0171-254 7429
(By appointment only)

'*Whither does he fly*' and '*The form of the god…*'. Two of the reliefs from the Aeneid Triptych by Harry Bates (1850 - 1899). Both signed 'HARRY BATES' and inscribed with a quotation from Virgil. One inscribed 'Anna, thou seest over att the shore how they are hastening / The whole bands are drawn together / The canvass now invites the gales / Why does he stop his unrepenting ear to my words / Whither does he fly'. The other entitled 'Aeneas', and inscribed 'Determined to depart was enjoying sleep in the lofty stern, / The form of the god returning with the same aspect appeared to him in his sleep'. Circa 1884 - 1885. Bronze. 22.5 x 48.5 cm (9 x 19 in).

Between 1883 and 1885, Bates worked in Paris where he was in contact with Rodin and Dalou. He returned to London in 1885, bringing back with him the panels known as the Aeneid reliefs, which he exhibited at the Royal Academy Exhibition of that year.

Only one other set of Aeneid panels is thought to exist and this is in the Glasgow City Art Gallery. There are examples of '*Whither does he fly*' in the National Musuem of Wales, Cardiff and in the Fitzwilliam Museum, Cambridge. No other examples of '*The form of the god…*' are known.

**Antoine Chenevière Fine Arts,
27 Bruton Street,
London W1X 7DB
Tel: 0171-491 1007
Fax: 0171- 495 6173**

One of a pair of Russian malachite and gilded bronze vases of the period of Tsar Alexander I. Circa 1820.
Height 56 cm (22 in).

These stone vases, of campana shape, are covered with a mosaic of malachite. The main copper mine in Russia was owned by Prince Demidoff, and it provided malachite for the Russian court.

In 1826, the sculptor William Theed the Younger went to Rome where he came under the influence of Bertel Thorwaldsen and John Gibson. Theed's work found particular favour with Queen Victoria and Prince Albert, and the many commissions he received through royal patronage included the figure of *Africa* for the *Albert Memorial* in Hyde Park, London.

Carved by Theed in Rome, *Psyche* is a fine example of the sculptor's late neo-classicism. In 1844, Prince Albert selected *Psyche* to be executed full-size for Osborne House on the Isle of Wight, and it was subsequently shown at the Royal Academy in 1845, no.1332.

The romance of Cupid and Psyche related by Apuleius in *The Golden Ass* is an allegory of the trials of the earthbound soul before its union with the divine after death. Until the 5th century BC, the soul was depicted as a bird or butterfly, encouraging post-classical artists to depict Psyche as a winged girl. In the tale, Psyche disobeys Cupid's instructions and he deserts her. Rather than represent Psyche's distress violently as described by Apuleius, Theed represents her contemplating her loss, lightly cradling the bow left behind by Cupid as he fled.

Joanna Barnes Fine Arts,
14 Mason's Yard,
Duke Street,
St James's,
London SW1Y 6BU
Tel: 0171-930 4215
Fax: 0171-839 8307

Psyche lamenting the Loss of Cupid by William Theed, the Younger (1804 - 1891). Signed 'W. Theed Fecit Roma 1842'. Marble. Height 105 cm (41 ½ in).

**Joanna Barnes Fine Arts,
14 Mason's Yard,
Duke Street,
St James's,
London SW1Y 6BU
Tel: 0171-930 4215
Fax: 0171-839 8307**

A Fox and Two Cubs by Joseph Gott (1786 - 1860). Signed 'J. GOTT Ft'. Marble. Height 57 cm (22 ½ in). Width 71 cm (28 in).

Apprenticed to the leading neo-classical sculptor, John Flaxman, from 1798 to 1802, Gott then exhibited regularly at the Royal Academy until 1822, when he went to Rome. Here he established a successful studio, and received much encouragement from the painter Sir Thomas Lawrence, who recommended him to many patrons including William, 6th Duke of Devonshire. The latter awarded Gott two important commissions, *A Bacchante* and *A Greyhound with her Two Puppies*. Following the great success of this *animalier* group, Gott produced a series of animal compositions, the majority of which included greyhounds. Later he began to vary the subject-matter of his animal sculpture and, through this facility in carving animals, became renowned as 'the Landseer of marble'.

A Fox and Two Cubs is a rare subject in the sculptor's *oeuvre*, and remained untraced for many years until its recent reappearance. The subject is first recorded in marble at the Royal Academy in 1848, no.1324, and then at the International Exhibition in London in 1862.

Victor Franses Gallery,
57 Jermyn Street,
St James's,
London SW1Y 6LX
Tel: 0171-493 6284
Fax: 0171-495 3668

A fine quality French mid 19th-century atelier bronze model of a stag, hind and calf by Antoine Louis Barye, (1796 - 1875), with a rich green and orange-brown patina. Signed 'Barye'.
Circa 1860.
Height 21 cm (8 ¼ in).
Length 25 cm (9 ¾ in).

One of the foremost sculptors of the 19th century, Barye was referred to by Rodin as the 'Father of French Sculpture'. Best known for his sculptures of wild animals and combat scenes, Barye was also adept at more tranquil subjects, as shown in this most successful composition.

Listed in Barye's catalogue of 1847, this model proved popular with collectors of the day, and was edited by Barye throughout his life. This present cast dates from the early 1860s, when Barye was finishing his models with individual and exotic patinas.

Victor Franses Gallery,
57 Jermyn Street,
St James's,
London SW1Y 6LX
Tel: 0171-493 6284
Fax: 0171-495 3668

A rare 19th-century French bronze model entitled *Trois Age*, by Pierre Lenordez, (1810 - 1896), with a medium brown patina. Signed 'P. Lenordez' and inscribed 'Duplan et Salles'. Circa 1860. Height including base 16 cm (6 ½ in). Length including base 25 cm (10 in).

One of the group of artists known as *Les Animaliers*, Lenordez was particularly adept at sculpting horses, especially those around the racetrack, and he completed many portraits of famous horses of the day.

This model is particularly unusual, both for its delicate size and for its subject matter – the three stages of a brood mare's life, foal, mother and protective great dam.

The best examples of Lenordez's work were cast by the small but high-quality foundry of Duplan et Salles, who were active in Paris in the 1860s and 1870s.

Grosvenor Antiques Ltd.,
27 Holland Street,
Kensington,
London W8 4NA
Tel: 0171-937 8649
Fax: 0171-937 7179

Pandora by Eugène-Antoine Aizelin (Paris 1821-1902), France, circa 1860. Silvered and gilded bronze. Signed 'AIZELIN'. Foundry mark: 'F. BARBEDIENNE FONDEUR' and the Collas seal. Height 50 cm (20 in). Base 15 x 12 cm (6 x 4 ³/₄ in).

Eugène-Antoine Aizelin was a pupil of Ramey and Dumont at the Ecole des Beaux- Arts and exhibited at the Salon from 1852. He won a second medal in 1878 and the Gold medal in 1889. He was an officer of the Legion of Honour.

The founders, Barbedienne, were established in Paris in 1838 and, in collaboration with Achille Collas, the inventor of a machine to reduce sculptures to various sizes, produced some of the finest bronze casts of the 19th century. *Pandora* appears in their catalogue for 1864.

Greek myth relates that Prometheus offended Zeus who, in revenge, created a beautiful girl to tempt him. He called her Pandora, the gift of all the gods. The wary Prometheus refused this gift but his brother, Epimetheus, fell in love with her. Pandora brought him her dowry in a casket which she was forbidden to open, but curiosity overcame her, and out flew dark and evil spirits. At the very bottom of the casket was a small, radiant, golden being whom the gods, with a touch of divine pity, had created to lighten the darkness and to chase away the evil spirits. Her name was Hope.

**Galerie Neuse Kunsthandel,
Contrescarpe 14,
28203 Bremen,
Germany
Tel: 49-421 32 56 42
Fax: 49-421 32 86 11**

A rare Italian bronze figure of
Pan by Giuseppe Piamontini
(1644 - Florence - 1742).
Height 44.5 cm (17 ½ in).
Provenance: Collection The
Hermitage, St Petersburg, before
1928; Collection David Daniels,
Minneapolis, 1980.
Literature: Catalogue *Kunstwerke
aus den Beständen Leningrader
Museen und Schlösser*. Berlin 1928.
Catalogue *Sculpture from the
David Daniels Collection*,
Minneapolis Institute
of Arts, 1979.

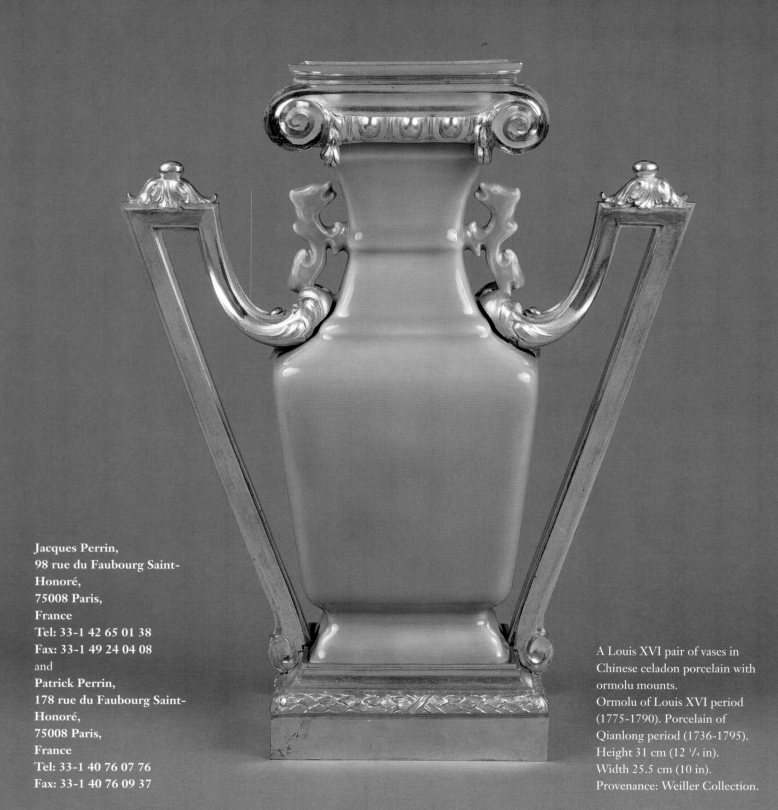

Jacques Perrin,
98 rue du Faubourg Saint-
Honoré,
75008 Paris,
France
Tel: 33-1 42 65 01 38
Fax: 33-1 49 24 04 08
and
Patrick Perrin,
178 rue du Faubourg Saint-
Honoré,
75008 Paris,
France
Tel: 33-1 40 76 07 76
Fax: 33-1 40 76 09 37

A Louis XVI pair of vases in
Chinese celadon porcelain with
ormolu mounts.
Ormolu of Louis XVI period
(1775-1790). Porcelain of
Qianlong period (1736-1795).
Height 31 cm (12 ¹/₄ in).
Width 25.5 cm (10 in).
Provenance: Weiller Collection.

Jacques Perrin,
98 rue du Faubourg Saint-
Honoré,
75008 Paris,
France
Tel: 33-1 42 65 01 38
Fax: 33-1 49 24 04 08
and
Patrick Perrin,
178 rue du Faubourg Saint-
Honoré,
75008 Paris,
France
Tel: 33-1 40 76 07 76
Fax: 33-1 40 76 09 37

One from a set of four ormolu
two-light sconces, attributed to
Philippe Caffieri (1714- 1774).
Louis XV period (1735-1775).
Height 53 cm (21 in).
Width 35 cm (13 ¾ in).
Literature: Hans Ottomayer and
Peter Proschel, *Vergoldete
Bronzen, die bronzearbeiten des
Spatbarock und Klassizismus*,
Munich 1986, II, S. 89 (Abb. X).
Similar sconces are in the
Kurfurstenzimmer of the
residence of Munich.

Richard Philp,
59 Ledbury Road,
London W11 2AA
Tel: 0171-727 7915
Fax: 0171-792 9073

A carved limewood figure with original polychrome. South German, circa 1480 - 1490. Height 94 cm (37 in).

This figure originates from the Tyrol area of Southern Germany, and shows the influence of Hans Klocker (fl.1478 – 1500) and Michael Pacher (fl. 1467 – 1475). A good point of comparison is provided by Klocker's *St George slaying the dragon*, formerly in the Staatliche Museen, Berlin (destroyed in the Second World War). (See G. Duby, *Sculpture: the great art of the Middle Ages from the 5th to the 15th century*, 1990, p. 271, illus.)

**The Temple Gallery,
6 Clarendon Cross,
Holland Park,
London W11 4AP
Tel: 0171-727 3809
Fax: 0171-727 1546**

St Nikita beating the devil.
Tempera and gesso on wood.
Russian, Moscow School. Middle
of the 16th century. Panel
56.5 x 41.7 cm (22 $\frac{1}{4}$ x 16 $\frac{3}{8}$ in).

The flat treatment of the composition, the balanced rhythm, absence of agitation, and the full rounded face of the saint, all suggest a Muscovite painter, perhaps influenced by the style of Dionisy, whose workshop was maintained by his sons for a generation after his death in 1501. These mannerisms can be seen in the frescoes of the Annunciation Cathedral in the Moscow Kremlin, dated 1547 - 1551 (see Kachalova, Mayasova and Shchennikova, *The Annunciation Cathedral of the Moscow Kremlin*, Isskustvo, 1990, pl. 21-106).

SEAGO

STAND 85

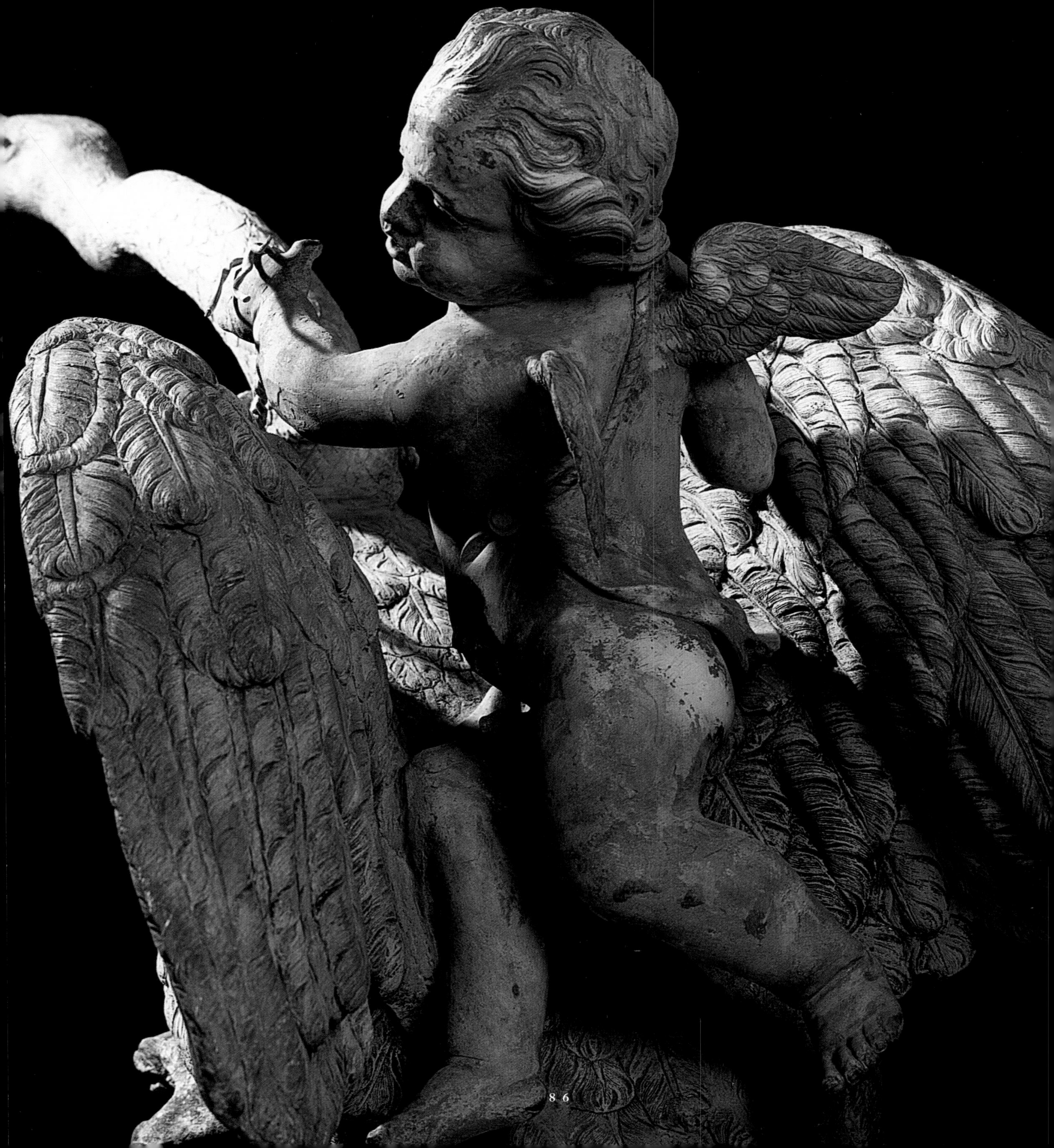

Seago,
22 Pimlico Road,
London SW1W 8LJ
Tel: 0171-730 7502
Fax: 0171-730 9179

Cupid and swan arising from reeds by John van Nost the Elder (d. 1710). Cast and chased lead, plumbed to spout water from the swan's mouth. English, circa 1700. Height 89 cm (35 in).

Width 64 cm (25 in).
Depth 127 cm (50 in).

The swan's beauty held great significance for classical writers, who described the creature's legendary love of music, and the beautiful song it sang at the end of its life. This musical connection accounts for its association with Apollo and certain Muses, particularly Erato and Clio, but may also be linked to

the fable about the soul of a poet entering into a swan. Undoubtedly the swan's beauty made it an appropriate attribute of Venus, and a pair of swans are often portrayed drawing her chariot. Here her offspring, Cupid, is depicted riding on the graceful creature's back.

The late 17th and early 18th centuries saw the zenith of lead production in England, with many original creations being designed,

cast, and finely chased by the highly skilled London artisans, Arnold Quellin (1653 - 1686), Andries Carpentiere (1670s - 1737), and Van Nost. Among the latter's more important commissions were gate finials for Hampton Court, and the huge vase depicting the four seasons at Melbourne Hall in Derbyshire. A similar example to the present sculpture may be seen at Rousham in Oxfordshire.

88

FURNITURE AND
ARCHITECTURAL ITEMS

tail of a pair of Chippendale
riod, gilded carved wood
andoles, circa 1760.
rman Adams Ltd

A late 17th-century Charles II
period silvered mirror, with
carved and pierced scroll
work frame, circa 1680.
Hotspur Ltd

One from a set of six Italian
carved giltwood chairs,
circa 1810.
Mallett

A Regency period kingwood
and gilt-metal mounted
end-support writing table,
circa 1800.
Apter-Fredericks Ltd

**Norman Adams Ltd.,
8-10 Hans Road,
London SW3 1RX**
(opp. west side of Harrods)
**Tel: 0171-589 5266
Fax: 0171-589 1968**

An outstanding George III oval purpleheart and marquetry Pembroke table.
English, circa 1775.
Height 71 cm (28 in).
Width 96.5 cm (38 in).
Depth 73 cm (29 in).
Provenance: probably the Earls of Crawford and Balcarres; the Earls of Portsmouth.

This form of oval Pembroke table, the outline echoed in a central patera, was popular at this period, as is evident from designs published in Hepplewhite's *Cabinet Maker and Upholsterer's Guide* (1788-94), but rarely is an example of such quality found.

The bold fan-patera, a neo-classical device derived from the sunflower motif of the Temple of Apollo at Palmyra, has a splendid *trompe-l'oeil* effect, achieved by subtly scorching segments of holly. It is surrounded by finely drawn and etched marquetry of urns, harebells and sinuous foliage, while the bowed ends are embellished with shells, palm fronds and anthemia, with bell-flower chains on the slender, tapered legs.

Comparisons may be drawn with marquetry pieces from the workshop of Thomas Chippendale, but certain distinctive features, such as the inclusion of berries on the foliage, do not seem to be part of that *oeuvre*.

A 19th-century panel, reused in the drawer lining, is painted on the underside with the crest of the Earls of Crawford and Balcarres, and the insignia of the Order of the Thistle. James Ludovic Lindsay, 26th Earl of Crawford and 9th Earl of Balcarres (1847-1913), was honoured as a member of this Order.

Norman Adams Ltd.,
8-10 Hans Road,
London SW3 1RX
(opp. west side of Harrods)
Tel: 0171-589 5266
Fax: 0171-589 1968

An unusually large, early George III carved mahogany tripod table with square top.
English, circa 1760.
Height 74 cm (29 in).
Width 86.5 cm (34 in).

Tripod tables are frequently depicted in 18th-century paintings of British interiors. Intended primarily as tea tables, they were also used as work tables and tables for informal breakfasts and suppers. This example, with its large square top, would lend itself well to the latter use.

The revolving tilt-top, on a birdcage support, has ribbon and flower edge-carving which, like the gadrooning on the baluster stem, remains particularly sharp, due to the fine timber used. The tripod base, with its well-drawn claw and ball feet, gives the table good balance.

**Norman Adams Ltd.,
8-10 Hans Road,
London SW3 1RX**
(opp. west side of Harrods)
**Tel: 0171-589 5266
Fax: 0171-589 1968**

A very fine early George III
carved mahogany semi-elliptical
serving table.
English, circa 1770.
Height 92 cm (36 in).
Width 183 cm (72 in).
Depth 67.2 cm (26 ¹/₂ in).

For a table of this size, the elegant
proportions, particularly the
depth, give a satisfying sense of
lightness. The rich colour and figured veneers are matched by great
refinement of detail such as the
slender mouldings round the top
and bottom edges of the frieze and
the wave-moulded tapered legs
headed with crisply-carved paterae
and ending with shaped feet
carved with smaller paterae. The
frieze between the front legs forms
the face of a drawer, the bottom of
the carved central tablet acting as
the pull. This table would almost
certainly have been made for a
dining room.

Luís Alegria,
Av. Dr Antunes Guimarães 142,
4100 Porto,
Portugal
Tel: 351-2 6182324
Fax: 351-2 6105446

A George II mahogany pole screen
with a Soho tapestry, circa 1755.
Provenance: reputedly Cusworth
Hall, Doncaster, Yorkshire.
Height 149 cm (58 ½ in).
Width 66cm (26 in).

Luís Alegria,
Av. Dr Antunes Guimarães 142,
4100 Porto,
Portugal
Tel: 351-2 6182324
Fax: 351-2 6105446

Two from a set of four French Louis XV walnut armchairs. Mid 18th century. One indistinctly signed 'I.Lebas', for Jean Baptiste Lebas, *reçu maître* 1756. Provenance: HRH Princess Christina of The Netherlands.

**Apter-Fredericks Ltd.,
265-267 Fulham Road,
London SW3 6HY
Tel: 0171-352 2188
Fax: 0171-376 5619**

A very rare carved mahogany breakfast table in the manner of Thomas Chippendale.
English, circa 1760.
Height 70 cm (27 ½ in).
Width 121 cm (47 ½ in).
Depth 109 cm (43 in).
Literature: Thomas Chippendale, *The Gentleman and Cabinet Maker's Director*, 1762, third edition, pl. LIII.

The design for this table appears in Thomas Chippendale's *Director* (pl. 53). It is very rare to find a piece of furniture which so closely approximates to an original design by one of the great cabinet-makers. In this instance, the marked similarity of design and the quality of both the mahogany and the carving indicate that the table probably originated in Chippendale's workshop.

**Apter-Fredericks Ltd.,
265-267 Fulham Road,
London SW3 6HY
Tel: 0171-352 2188
Fax: 0171-376 5619**

An important George III mahogany breakfront cabinet. English, circa 1790.
Height 231 cm (91 in).
Width 146 cm (57 ¼ in).
Depth 58.5 cm (23 in).

This cabinet, which is of extremely rare design, is in pristine condition. The glazed upper section with original painted decoration is surmounted by two carved urn-shaped finials. The lower section has finely figured oval panels to each door, and a recessed kneehole cupboard in the centre.

This cabinet was exhibited at the 1949 Grosvenor House Antiques Fair and was illustrated in the Handbook.

Asprey,
165-169 New Bond Street,
London W1Y 0AR
Tel: 0171-493 6767
Fax: 0171-491 0384

A magnificent Louis XIV tortoiseshell and marquetry cabinet on stand, known as the Merry Cabinet, attributed to Pierre Gole, *ébéniste du Roi*.
Height 188 cm (74 in).
Width 142 cm (56 in).
Depth 51 cm (20 in).
Provenance: Acquired by James Merry, MP (1805-1877); given by him to his niece in 1862 on her marriage to one of his Parliamentary colleagues; thence by family descent.
Literature: A. Pradère, *French Furniture Makers*, 1989, fig. 4.
M. Riccardi-Cubitt, *The Art of the Cabinet*, 1992, fig. 53.

The inventory of Cardinal Mazarin's collection of 1661 mentioned two cabinets of a similar description made by Gole (Th. H. Lunsingh Scheurleer, 'The Philippe D'Orleans ivory cabinet by Pierre Gole', *Burlington Magazine*, June 1984). These cabinets were acquired by Mazarin between 1653 and 1661. The Duc D'Orleans cabinet can be seen at the Victoria and Albert Museum.

**Avon Antiques,
25, 26 & 27 Market Street,
Bradford on Avon,
Wiltshire
BA15 1LL
Tel: 01225-862052
Fax: 01225-862937**

A George III satinwood dressing table, crossbanded in palisander wood. Circa 1790 - 1795.
Height 87 cm (34 in).
Width (open) 119 cm (47 in).
Depth 49 cm (19 in).

Provenance: By descent until 1992, this table formed part of the furnishings of Bridwell House, Uffculme, Devon. Literature: A.P. Hughes, *Short History of Bridwell and the Family of Clarke*. John Cornforth,

'Bridwell, Devon', *Country Life*, March 1981. Furniture History Society, '*Dictionary of English Furniture Makers*', 1986, p. 796-797. Furniture History Society, '*Pictorial Dictionary of Marked London Furniture*'.

In March 1793, the well-known London cabinetmaking partnership of Seddon, Sons and Shackleton supplied furniture to Richard Hall Clarke Esq. for his new neo-classical mansion at

Bridwell. Some bills of the commission survive for the drawing room furniture, including those for a Pembroke table and a pair of card tables in satinwood crossbanded in palisander wood with painted decoration. This dressing table is in the manner of Seddon, and its date and stylistic details, including the distinctive gilt-brass handles, suggest that it was part of the commission.

Avon Antiques,
25, 26 & 27 Market Street,
Bradford on Avon,
Wiltshire
BA15 1LL
Tel: 01225-862052
Fax: 01225-862937

A George II mahogany rent table with leather-lined and crossbanded revolving top with a lidded centre well, worked by a secret spring-loaded catch. The revolving top has twelve wedge-shaped drawers for estate account documents and monies. The drawers are arranged alphabetically, with bone inlaid initials and swan-neck handles. The square base has four figured panels, one concealing a cupboard, and canted corners with blind fretwork in the Chinese manner. The table stands on ogee bracket feet, decorated with carved acanthus and clover leaves. Circa 1765. Height 79 cm (31 in). Diameter 107 cm (42 in). Literature: Similar pieces are illustrated in Cescinsky, *English Furniture, Gothic to Sheraton*, 1937, p. 357 and C. Claxton Stevens and S. Whittington, *18th Century English Furniture*, 1983, p. 110.

Avon Antiques,
25, 26 & 27 Market Street,
Bradford on Avon,
Wiltshire
BA15 1LL
Tel: 01225-862052
Fax: 01225-862937

A William and Mary burr yew lowboy, circa 1690.
Height 73 cm (28 ³/₄ in).
Width 74 cm (29 in).
Depth 47 cm (19 in).

This table shows particular attention to design and detail. On the top, burr yew veneers radiate from a centre sunburst in holly and pearwood. Below is an arched, serpentine-shaped frieze edged in hornbeam and with two

yew pendants. The cupped and turned legs are tied by serpentine stretchers with two finials. The table has the original handles and bun feet.

ANTOINE CHENEVIÈRE FINE ARTS

**Antoine Chenevière Fine Arts,
27 Bruton Street,
London W1X 7DB
Tel: 0171-491 1007
Fax: 0171- 495 6173**

A Russian round neo-classical gueridon in mahogany and gilded bronze, the top in grey granite from Finland. Attributed to Christian Meyer. Circa 1805. Height 79 cm (31 in). Diameter 48 cm (19 in).

Christian Meyer was a carpentry teacher, and cabinetmaker to the Grand Dukes Alexander and Constantine of Russia. He worked for important palaces including the Hermitage, the Mikhailovsky Castle, and Pavlovsk Palace.

H.C. Baxter & Sons

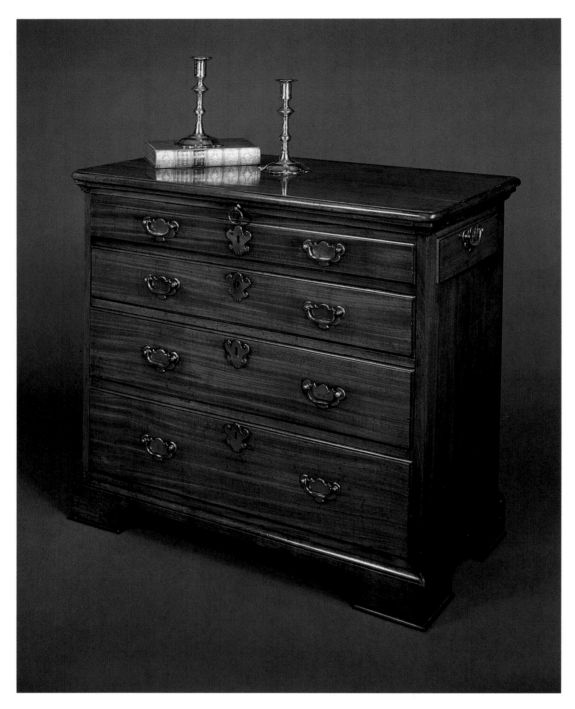

H.C. Baxter & Sons,
40 Drewstead Road,
London SW16 1AB
Tel: 0181-769 5969
Fax: 0181-769 0898

An outstanding George II
mahogany chest of small size,
retaining its original brasswork.
Circa 1740.
Height 75 cm (29 ½ in).
Width 81 cm (32 in).
Depth 43 cm (17 in).
Provenance: The collection of
David Style Esq., Wateringbury
Place, Maidstone, Kent.

The arrangement of drawers is
most unusual in this chest.
Beneath the moulded top is a full
width brushing slide, flanked by a
drawer to either side of the chest.
The top drawer at the front is
therefore false.

H.C. Baxter & Sons

**H.C. Baxter & Sons,
40 Drewstead Road,
London SW16 1AB
Tel: 0181-769 5969
Fax: 0181-769 0898**

A very rare pair of Regency tripod tables, made of solid rosewood. Circa 1820. Height 76 cm (30 in). Diameter 38 cm (15 in).

These tables, probably by Gillow, have an exceptional patina. The dished tops are of a most unusual shape.

**H. Blairman & Sons,
119 Mount Street,
London W1Y 5HB
Tel: 0171-493 0444
Fax: 0171-495 0766**

A refectory table designed by
A.W.N. Pugin (1812-1852).
Oak, with pine base.
English, circa 1840-41.
Height 73.7 cm (29 in).
Width 122.6 cm (48 ¼ in).

Length 287 cm (113 in).
Provenance: Convent of Our
Lady of Mercy, Handsworth,
Birmingham.

The design of this refectory table
seems accurately to reflect Pugin's
contemporary proclamation: 'The
two great rules for design are
these: 1st, that there should be no
features about a building [and this
applies equally to furniture]

which are not necessary for con-
venience, construction, or "propriety"; 2nd, that all ornament
should consist of enrichment of
the essential construction...'.
(*True Principals of Pointed or
Christian Architecture*, London,
1841). The lack of ornament on
the present table epitomises
Pugin's mature style (see, for
example, *Pugin: a Gothic Passion*,
ed. Paul Atterbury and Clive

Wainwright, London and New
Haven, 1994, figs. 241-244).

John Hardman (1767-1844),
who paid for the building and
furnishing of the convent in
Hunter's Road, Handsworth, was
one of Pugin's most trusted
collaborators. As 'Mediaeval
Metalworkers' and stained glass
manufacturers in Birmingham,
Hardmans executed many of
Pugin's designs.

**H. Blairman & Sons,
119 Mount Street,
London W1Y 5HB
Tel: 0171-493 0444
Fax: 0171-495 0766**

A ceremonial armchair.
Beech, gilded; the upholstery of
later date. The front seat rail has
a partial inventory in ink on a
heart-shaped paper label, and a
printed label with the arms of
Sir Charles Stuart, and his
name in ink.
English (London), circa 1815.
Height 121.9cm (48 in).
Width 68.6 cm (27 in).
Depth 52.7 cm (20 ³/₄in).
Provenance: Sir Charles Stuart,
later Lord Stuart de Rothesay
(1779-1845).

This large chair was probably
supplied to Sir Charles Stuart in
1815, when he was appointed
Ambassador Extraordinary and
Plenipotentiary to Paris. The
label, which appears on other
furniture once owned by Sir
Charles when he was at the Hôtel
de Charôst, is thought to have
been placed on the chair ('*Trone*')
during an inventory taken on
20 August 1816 by the Parisian
marchand de meubles Michelot (see
Sarah Medlam, *The Bettine, Lady
Abingdon Collection…*, London,
1996, p. 48, F. 4 and fig. 26).

   An ambassadorial chair of
almost identical design, two large
stools and a footstool, all *en suite*,
are at Knole. These pieces are
thought to have been supplied to
Lord Whitworth (1752-1825) in
1802, on his appointment as
ambassador to Paris. Payments in

the Lord Chamberlain's Account
Book for the years 1800-1811
indicate that this furniture may
have been either by 'Mr Russell,
Joiner', or by 'Mr Adair, Carver
& Gilder' (see Martin Drury,
'Two Georgian Chairs of State…
at Knole', *Furniture History XXI*,
1985, p. 243-249). William Adair
worked from Wardour Street,
London and John Russell probably from Bird Street, London.

**Richard Courtney Ltd.,
112-114 Fulham Road,
London SW3 6HU
Tel. and Fax: 0171-370 4020**

A rare, near pair of William and Mary veneered walnut demi-lune card tables with feather-banded and cross-banded hinged tops, the frieze with a centre drawer and dummy drawers at the sides, and a shaped apron below, on baluster legs and bun feet, and with gate-leg action at the back to support the top when open. English, circa 1690.
Height 74 cm (29 in).
Width 81 cm (32 in).
Depth 33 cm (13 in).

This is the earliest type of card table introduced in the late 17th century, and it is unusual to find a pair.

**Richard Courtney Ltd.,
112-114 Fulham Road,
London SW3 6HU
Tel. and Fax: 0171-370 4020**

A fine George I veneered burr walnut bureau cabinet in two parts, the upper part with mirrored doors above sliding candlestands, the interior with various small drawers, pigeonholes, adjustable folio-racks and a centre door. The bureau opens to reveal a fitted interior with small drawers and pigeonholes, a well, and a centre door with dummy leather books to either side concealing secret drawers. English, circa 1720. Height 208 cm (82 in). Width 99 cm (39 in). Depth 59 cm (23 1/4 in).

The burr walnut used in this piece is of the finest quality and of excellent faded colour, figuring and patination. The doors, drawers, and bureau-flap are all feather-banded and cross-banded. An interesting feature is the waist moulding which is a survival from earlier times when bureaux divided at this point for ease of carriage.

Richard Courtney Ltd.,
112-114 Fulham Road,
London SW3 6HU
Tel. and Fax: 0171-370 4020

A fine George I veneered walnut kneehole desk of superb colour and patination, the top quarter-veneered and with feather-banding and cross-banding, the corners inverted. In the recess is a door, also feather-banded, with cupboard behind. All drawers retain their original handles. English, circa 1720.
Height 73 cm (28 ³/₄ in).
Width 89 cm (35 in).
Depth 46 cm (18 in).

The kneehole desk was introduced in the early part of the 18th century, and was the forerunner of the pedestal desk. The fluted, canted corners are an unusual feature of this example.

**Richard Courtney Ltd.,
112-114 Fulham Road,
London SW3 6HU
Tel. and Fax: 0171-370 4020**

A fine Anglo-Indian Vizagapatam ivory and sandalwood miniature bureau cabinet with a broken pediment bearing a crest of lions, the upper part with doors to either side enclosing small drawers and pigeonholes, and with central drawers showing houses and river and village scenes, all with foliate borders. The bureau flap is decorated with the motif of a palace, enclosing a fitted interior with solid ivory pilasters concealing drawers. Vizagapatam, circa 1790.
Height 93 cm (36 1/2 in).
Width 60 cm (23 3/4 in).
Depth 27 cm (10 1/2 in).

From the middle of the 18th century, Indian works of art became highly popular in Europe. Vizagapatam, on the east coast of India between Calcutta and Madras, offered easy access to cargo ships on their way back from the Far East. The craftsmen incised and lac-filled the ivory, often using pictures of houses or other motifs previously sent out from Europe.

Devenish,
929 Madison Avenue,
New York,
N.Y. 10021,
U.S.A.
Tel: 212-535 2888
Fax: 212-535 2889

A fine and rare pair of George III giltwood window seats, attributed to Thomas Chippendale, circa 1770.
Height (maximum) 66 cm (26 in).
Length 117 cm (46 in).
Depth 49.5 cm (19 ½ in).
Provenance: Almost certainly supplied to Sir Robert Burdett,

4th Bt. (1716 - 1797) of Foremark Hall, Derbyshire. Thence by descent until sold from Foremark Hall circa 1939. Exhibited: A window seat from this suite was exhibited at Christies, London, Chippendale Loan Exhibition.

These window seats have provenance from Foremark Hall, Derbyshire, and almost certainly formed part of the house's original furnishings. Foremark Hall was built in 1759 - 1761 for Sir Robert Burdett, 4th Bt., following his marriage in 1753 to

Catherine Manners, daughter of the 2nd Duke of Rutland. The decoration of the interior continued over a period of more than twenty years, involving the commissioning of large quantities of furniture. Furnishing accounts for Foremark Hall (held in Berkshire Record Office) confirm that much of this furniture was supplied by Thomas Chippendale, who, between 1766 and 1774, received a total of over £800, indicating a commission of considerable size and importance.

The present window seats almost certainly formed part of

the furnishings supplied by Chippendale, having marked stylistic affinities with other examples of his work. A closely related pair of window stools, almost certainly supplied by Chippendale for Harewood House, Yorkshire, is illustrated in Christopher Claxton Stevens and Stewart Whittington, *18th Century Furniture, The Norman Adams Collection*, 1983, p. 62.

The contents of Foremark Hall were largely dispersed in a sale in 1939, and it is believed the present window seats left the house at this date.

Devenish,
929 Madison Avenue,
New York,
N.Y. 10021,
U.S.A.
Tel: 212-535 2888
Fax: 212-535 2889

A highly important pair of
Chinese export mirror paintings
in exceptionally fine George II
carved gesso and giltwood
frames. Circa 1755.
Height 178 cm (70 in).
Width 101.6 cm (40 in).

Literature: F.L. Hinckley, *Queen
Anne and Georgian Looking
Glasses*, 1987, fig. 216 and
cover illus.

This is possibly the only
surviving pair of such mirrors, of
this quality and in this condition.

Devenish,
929 Madison Avenue,
New York,
N.Y. 10021, U.S.A.
Tel: 212-535 2888
Fax: 212-535 2889

One of a highly important pair of George III carved and gilded pier mirrors in the manner of John Linnell. The original surmount of a basket of flowers is not shown. English, circa 1765.

Height 269 cm (106 in).
Width 147 cm (58 in).
Provenance: J. Paul Getty, Sutton Place, Guildford, Surrey.
Literature: Christopher Claxton Stevens and Stewart Whittington,

18th Century English Furniture, The Norman Adams Collection, 1983, p. 427 illustrates an identical mirror.

Michael Foster,
118 Fulham Road,
London SW3 6HU
Tel: 0171-373 3636
Fax: 0171-373 4042

A superb set of eighteen Hepplewhite mahogany shield-back dining room chairs, raised on tapering moulded legs. The back splats of complex pierced form incorporate a classical Adam urn, paterae, flower heads, foliage, and a beaded oval. English, circa 1790.

Hepplewhite was both a designer and a maker of chairs. As the Prince of Wales was one of his patrons, he particularly favoured the Prince's famous three feather emblem. Although he was not the originator of the design, Hepplewhite interpreted the oval, heart-shaped and shield-back chairs to perfection, and his name is synonymous with the distinctive style of light and elegant furniture fashionable at the end of the 18th century.

Hepplewhite was apprenticed to Gillows of Lancaster before moving to London about 1760, where he opened a shop in Redcross Street, St Giles, Cripplegate. He died in 1786, and his book, *The Cabinet Maker and Upholsterer's Guide*, was published posthumously by his widow, Alice, in 1788. This book illustrates some 300 designs which epitomise the neo-classical style and employ Robert Adam's principle of combining elegance and utility. The chair shown here exemplifies these ideas.

Michael Foster,
118 Fulham Road,
London SW3 6HU
Tel: 0171-373 3636
Fax: 0171-373 4042

A George II carved and giltwood overmantle of architectural form in the manner of William Kent. English, circa 1720.

Height 128 cm (50 ½ in).
Width 162.5 cm (64 in).

The dimensions of this mirror indicate that it was made for a substantial chimney piece. Such mirrors were fashioned to integrate with the design of a room.

The pre-eminent designer in this field was William Kent

(1686 - 1748), who decorated interiors and designed furniture and objects to complete a unified scheme. His designs included elaborate carving of foliage, flowers, and masks, and were always large in scale, which suited the requirements of his patrons.

The motif emblematic of

Plenty (indicated by the central basket of wheat, flanked by male masks supporting garlands) is superbly carved. Architectural furniture of this type is in the grand tradition from classical Rome, through Palladio to William Kent.

Michael Foster,
118 Fulham Road,
London SW3 6HU
Tel: 0171-373 3636
Fax: 0171-373 4042

A George III giltwood and painted settee in the manner of George Seddon. English, circa 1800.
Height 94 cm (37 in).
Width 183 cm (72 in).
Depth 66 cm (26 in).

The influence of Robert Adam, and of French late 18th-century decoration, are apparent in the neo-classical design and orna-ments of this settee – ram's heads, swags and drapes, sunbursts, and turned spiral legs decorated with acanthus leaves. The ends of the settee also reflect late Louis-Seize and *Directoire* influence.

Many of the finest examples of formal salon seat furniture display neo-classical ornament, a fact illustrated by items supplied to important country houses and to Buckingham Palace. This sofa is a restrained and elegant English example of the fashion.

French neo-classicism, *Directoire*, and early Empire designs became all the rage throughout Europe and Russia. Thomas Sheraton s *Cabinet Maker and Upholsterer's Drawing Book* (1791 - 1794) abounded with designs inspired by those of late 18th-century France, in some cases indistinguishable from the originals, but in others showing an English interpretation. (Op. cit. part I, pl. 31; Appendix, pl. 2; Accompaniment, pl. 4, chair legs.)

The vogue for neo-classicism was adopted by other, and later, designers and cabinet makers of seat furniture – notably Henry Holland, George Smith, Morel and Hughes, Morel and Seddon. The last two firms mentioned were suppliers to the Royal Household.

Galerie Gismondi,
20 Rue Royale,
75008 Paris,
France
Tel: 33-1 42 60 73 89
Fax: 33-1 42 60 98 94

A Louis XIV Boulle marquetry
chessboard of tortoiseshell, red
horn, brass, pewter and olive
wood. French, circa 1675.
64 x 64 cm (25 ¼ x 25 ¼ in).
Provenance: Princes Thurn und
Taxis, The Silver Room of St
Emmeram Castle, Regensburg,
Bavaria.

**Galerie Gismondi,
20 Rue Royale,
75008 Paris,
France
Tel: 33-1 42 60 73 89
Fax: 33-1 42 60 98 94**

A very rare and important Empire mahogany armchair, the padded arms carved in the form of two seated, winged lions, ending with claw feet. Stamped by Francois Loret, who worked in Paris during the Empire period and the Restauration. French, circa 1811. Height 103 cm (40 ½ in). Literature: D. Ledoux-Lebard, *Les Ebenistes du XIXe Siècle 1795-1889, leurs oeuvres et leurs marques*, Paris 1965, p. 444-445.

Jonathan Harris,
9 Lower Addison Gardens,
London W14 8BG
Tel: 0171-602 6255
Fax: 0171-602 0488

A large mahogany rent table on pedestal base, the tooled leather top with a gilt-metal-bound edge, the frieze with eight cedar-lined drawers, cock-beaded with brass.
English, circa 1815.
Height 81 cm (32 in).
Diameter 137 cm (54 in).

The same castors and brass-bound cedar-lined drawers are found on a rosewood drum table illustrated in Christopher Claxton Stevens and Stewart Whittington, *Eighteenth Century English Furniture, The Norman Adams Collection*, 1983, col. pl. 15, p. 153.

**Jonathan Harris,
9 Lower Addison Gardens,
London W14 8BG
Tel: 0171-602 6255
Fax: 0171-602 0488**

A French Empire mahogany fall-front secretaire of exceptional quality, the arcaded interior veneered with amboyna, the pillars with gilt-metal capitals and bases, standing on a parquetry base. Circa 1815.
Height 142 cm (56 in).
Width 98 cm (38 ½ in).
Depth 49.5 cm (19 ½ in).

A similarly unstamped secretaire of like quality at Powis Castle, Powys, has an almost identical interior.

**Hotspur Ltd.,
14 Lowndes Street,
London SW1X 9EX
Tel: 0171-235 1918
Fax: 0171-235 4371**

An outstanding 18th-century George III period carved giltwood mirror of the finest quality, based upon a design by John Linnell. English, circa 1765.
Height 194 cm (76 ½ in).
Width 100 cm (39 ½ in).
Literature: Hayward and Kirkham, *William and John Linnell*, p. 96, fig. 186.

The superb giltwood border-glass frame is richly carved, pierced and undercut in rococo taste of the greatest delicacy, and is surmounted by a basket of flowers. The mirror glasses are original.

Hotspur Ltd.,
14 Lowndes Street,
London SW1X 9EX
Tel: 0171-235 1918
Fax: 0171-235 4371

An exceptionally fine 18th-century George III period mahogany settee of Hepplewhite design in the French taste. English, circa 1785.
Height 91 cm (35 ³/₄ in).

Width 213.5 cm (84 in).
Depth 85 cm (33 ¹/₂ in).

The well-shaped, serpentine upholstered frame has a camel back and elegant mahogany out-swept scrolling arms. It is raised on eight gracefully carved and moulded cabriole legs with cone feet, linked by serpentine-shaped aprons, carved and moulded with C-scrolls and foliage.

Jeremy Ltd.,
29 Lowndes Street,
London SW1X 9HX
Tel: 0171-823 2923
Fax: 0171-245 6197

An extremely rare French Empire kettle with the original brazier on tripod base, the whole executed in tôle, and retaining a major proportion of the original simulated aventurine and japanned decoration. Circa 1810. Maximum height 91.5 cm (36 in). Width 37 cm (14 ½ in). Depth 37 cm (14 ½ in).

The brazier on tripod base is in the form of an *athénienne*, a design after the Antique which was particularly popular during the French Empire period. On page 47 of Madeleine Deschamps' book, *Empire*, there is an illustration of the dining room at Malmaison, decorated by Percier and Fontaine, designers to Napoleon and creators of the Empire style. The walls of the dining room are decorated with Pompean-style murals, two of which depict a pair of *athéniennes* very similar in design to this brazier.

Tea was an expensive commodity at this time and, during the Empire period in France, it was the fashion in grand houses to drink tea on returning home from the theatre, while continuing the evening's conversations. Tea was accompanied by confections such as gingerbread, nougats, mixed sweets, and other sugary delicacies.

**Jeremy Ltd.,
29 Lowndes Street,
London SW1X 9HX
Tel: 0171-823 2923
Fax: 0171-245 6197**

A magnificent English George III period carved wood and gilded girandole with triple candle arms, the design in the manner of William France.
Circa 1765.
Height 150 cm (59 in).
Width 86 cm (34 in).

In the Gallery at Aske Hall, the Yorkshire seat of the Marquess of Zetland, hang a pair of girandoles of practically the same design as this.

It is known that Sir Lawrence Dundas employed more than one cabinetmaker to help him furnish his various houses, and Robert Adam probably advised him on his choice. Amongst the small number of eminent 18th-century craftsmen who worked on such houses as 19 Arlington Street (Sir Lawrence Dundas's London house), and his equally important country house at Moore Park, was the highly successful partnership of John Bradburn and William France. In France's accounts, of June 1764, to Sir Lawrence Dundas, it is interesting to note the entry which states, 'For 2 elegant carved Girandoles with a large plate of glass, and 3 lights in each to shew the glass, festoons and drops of husks falling from Different parts all gilt in burnished Gold at £28 6s. £56 12s.' In his article, 'Some Rococo Cabinet-Makers and Sir Lawrence Dundas' (*Apollo*, September 1967), Anthony Coleridge states that William France's invoice seems to correspond in every detail to the pair of mirrors now in the Gallery at Aske Hall, and it would therefore be very reasonable to suppose that they are the ones supplied by France.

**Jeremy Ltd.,
29 Lowndes Street,
London SW1X 9HX
Tel: 0171-823 2923
Fax: 0171-245 6197**

One from a set of twelve Chinese export dining chairs executed in figured and faded padoukwood, the pierced backs, shaped seats and cabriole front legs being carved with stylised lotus flowers and scroll work in the Chinese interpretation of English gesso-work. Circa 1740.
Height (back) 99 cm (39 in).
Height (seat) 45 cm (17 ½ in).
Width (seat) 54 cm (21 in).
Depth (seat) 47 cm (18 ½ in).
Literature: for illustrations of a similar model see:
Carl L. Crossman, *The Decorative Arts of the China Trade*, p.231, pl.83, and p. 229. Herbert Cescinsky, *English Furniture of the Eighteenth Century*, vol. II, p. 51, fig. 45.
A similar large set of dining chairs is in the Winter Dining Room at Hatfield House, seat of the Marquess of Salisbury.
Exhibited: Sothebys London, 'A Tale of Three Cities' exhibition, January 1997, cat. no. 218.

The very important and extensive trade between the Orient (China in particular) and Europe was initiated by the Portuguese as early as 1514 but it was not until 1715 that the British East India Company opened a 'factory' at Canton and placed the 'China Trade' on a stable footing. The town became the principal, and, after 1757, the only, port for the Chinese foreign trade, with the British taking a lion's share of the market. In 1753, out of 27 ships lying in the port, ten of the merchantmen were English. Of the many East India Companies, the English were 'the proudest society of merchants in the Universe'.

Jeremy Ltd,
29 Lowndes Street,
London SW1X 9HX
Tel: 0171-823 2923
Fax: 0171-245 6197

A highly important and rare Russian 18th-century polished steel and ormolu footstool with finely engraved decoration, from the workshops of the Tula Armourers. Circa 1750. Height 21 cm (8 ¼ in). Width 38 cm (15 in). Depth 30 cm (11 ¾ in).

This is one of the earliest Tula stools we have encountered, and must have been made for the Russian Imperial family. A later example, in polished and faceted steel and ormolu, was part of a set bought by Catherine the Great in 1789 at the fair held annually near Tsarsköe Selo, and is now in the Pavlovsk Palace Museum. It is illustrated in Antoine Chenevière, *Russian Furniture: The Golden Age 1780 - 1840*, Weidenfeld & Nicholson, London, 1988, p. 250, pl. 269.

Among the works of Russian

applied art of the 18th and early 19th centuries, the articles made from steel by the Tula Armourers occupy a special place. The Tula Arms Factory was founded in 1712 and in time the town became the centre of Russian arms production. In the second quarter of the 18th century, orders were frequently placed for richly decorated hunting weapons and for objects intended as gifts for representatives of foreign countries. The latter probably explains the presence of works of art from Tula in the collections of foreign museums.

A·WEISWEILER

Michael Lipitch Ltd.,
98 Fulham Road,
London SW3 6HS
Tel: 0171-589 7327
Fax: 0171-823 9106

A French mahogany writing table stamped on the underside 'A. Weisweiler', for Adam Weisweiler, working circa 1778 - 1809. The table retains its original leather top and ormolu mounts, and is fitted with a drawer at either end. Circa 1800.
Height 76.5 cm (30 $\frac{1}{4}$ in).
Length 93 cm (36 $\frac{1}{2}$ in).
Width 65.5 cm (25 $\frac{3}{4}$ in).
Provenance: Property of the Sturt family.

Adam Weisweiler was one of the most important cabinet-makers of his time. He was born in about 1750 at Neuwied on the Rhine where he studied in the workshop of David Roentgen (1743 - 1807). He was established in Paris as an *artisan-libre* early in the reign of Louis XVI, and was made *mâitre-ébéniste* in 1778. He seems to have done much work for D. Daguerre, through whose agency he supplied a considerable amount of furniture to the royal palaces, especially the Chateau de Saint-Cloud. Weisweiler's work can be seen in the Louvre, the Musée Cognac-Jay, Paris, Windsor Castle and the Wallace Collection, London.

The elegance and high quality that are associated with Weisweiler's work are particularly apparent in this writing table. Most noteworthy are the elegant proportions, pronounced tapering of the reeded legs, and the restrained treatment of the ormolu mounts.

Michael Lipitch Ltd.,
98 Fulham Road,
London SW3 6HS
Tel: 0171-589 7327
Fax: 0171-823 9106

A magnificent Irish hexagonal lantern, retaining its original lacquered brass finish. The upper section is divided into two tiers, with stylised acanthus motifs at the corners. Circa 1810.
Height 153 cm (60 in).
Diameter 79 cm (31 in).
Provenance: An important private country estate in Ireland.

Originally designed to hang in the entrance hall of a large country house, this lantern is distinguished by its size, the bold simplicity of its design, and the high quality of its decorative mounts. At present, the only other comparable example known (which has one upper tier instead of two) is the lantern hanging in the entrance hall of Goodwood House, which is illustrated in Charles Latham, *In English Homes*, 1904, p. 146.

Michael Lipitch Ltd,
98 Fulham Road,
London SW3 6HS
Tel: 0171-589 7327
Fax: 0171-823 9106

An English Regency lacquered casket in the Central Asian taste, supported on gilt-metal ball feet. The two doors open to reveal three drawers, each decorated with exotic birds and flowers. Circa 1810.
Height: 38.5 cm (15 in).
Width: 35 cm (13 ¾ in).
Depth: 23 cm (9 in).

The lacquered scenes are of the finest quality and are jewel-like in their colour and detail.

Caskets like this were generally used as receptacles for precious possessions. The iconography and quality of this example suggest it may have been a gift to an important Asian dignitary.

Michael Lipitch Ltd.,
98 Fulham Road,
London SW3 6HS
Tel: 0171-589 7327
Fax: 0171-823 9106

A George I walnut pedestal kneehole dressing table retaining its original handles and raised on the original bracket feet.
Circa 1720.
Height 79 cm (31 ¼ in).

Width 75 cm (29 ½ in).
Depth 45.5 cm (18 in).

The distinguishing feature of this desk is the rich, untouched patina, built up over many years.

**Peter Lipitch Ltd.,
120 & 124 Fulham Road,
London SW3 6HU
Tel: 0171-373 3328
Fax: 0171-373 8888**

A George III satinwood and sabicu china cabinet, circa 1795.
Height 207 cm (81 ½ in).
Width 85.5 cm (33 ¾ in).
Depth 47 cm (18 ½ in).

This cabinet is of a form, made by the Seddons company in the last quarter of the 18th century, with the unusual feature of a recessed cupboard to the lower section. The cabinet is veneered in highly figured West Indian (San Domingo) satinwood with tulipwood and purpleheart banding and sabicu panels. The upper section has a 'pear-drop' cornice above Gothic-shaped veneered glazing bars. The lower section has a drawer, retaining its original handles, above three panelled cupboards, and stands on square tapered feet with garter toes.

Peter Lipitch Ltd.,
120 & 124 Fulham Road,
London SW3 6HU
Tel: 0171-373 3328
Fax: 0171-373 8888

A rare pair of mahogany armchairs attributed to Thomas Chippendale. Circa 1775. Height 91 cm (35 ¾ in). Width 59 cm (23 ¼ in). Provenance: From the estate of Louisa Heathcote, Friday Hill House, Chingford, Essex, a descendant of Sir Gilbert Heathcote. Sir Gilbert was a major patron of Chippendale and commissioned him to supply furniture for his residence at Normanton Hall, Rutland, and his town houses in Fulham and Grosvenor Square; Chippendale's company also furnished and directed the funeral of Sir Gilbert's mother in 1772. These chairs were probably supplied to Conington Castle, Huntingdon, for Sir Gilbert's brother, John Heathcote, and thence by descent.

These chairs, executed in dense Cuban mahogany and with finely defined carving, are a familiar Chippendale pattern with elements unique to his work: the tapered, reeded therm legs and the carved acanthus-leaf cup brackets to the base of the arm supports are distinctive features, and confirm his authorship. Chippendale did not repeat his models exactly; the inlaid boxwood cartouches in the cresting rails of these chairs are an interesting variation on the more usual carved cartouches.

A very similar pair of the same model, in giltwood, were supplied by Chippendale to Lord Egremont of Egremont House in 1777. These are illustrated in Christopher Gilbert, *The Life and Work of Thomas Chippendale*, pl. 187.

Mallett,
Bourdon House,
2 Davies Street,
London W1Y 1LJ
Tel: 0171-629 2444
Fax: 0171-499 2670

A most unusual Charles X mahogany oval jardiniere on stand, attributed to Caron the elder. The jardiniere is in the form of a *lit en bateau*, and the base forms a Gothic colonnaded oval, inlaid with boxwood stringing, standing on a shaped plinth. French, circa 1825.
Height 96 cm (38 in).
Width 80 cm (31 ½ in).
Depth 49 cm (19 ½ in).

Caron the elder worked at 123 rue du Faubourg St Antoine until his death in January 1838. During the 1830s, he published a series of small books illustrating furniture designs for cabinetmakers, while also supplying furniture both within France and abroad. In 1837, he was commissioned by the *Garde Meuble*, as a designer-cabinetmaker, to supply a number of pieces of furniture.

The designs illustrated in his works are eclectic, many being of Gothic or Renaissance inspiration, with elaborate linear geometric inlays in light boxwood on a dark, frequently rosewood, ground.

Mallett,
141 New Bond Street,
London W1Y 0BS
Tel: 0171-499 7411
Fax: 0171-495 3179

A very rare pair of early 18th-century giltwood torchères, the trefoil tops carved with lambrequins and raised on S-shaped stems with elaborated floral and foliate carving and scrolling tripod bases.
Wurzburg, circa 1720.
Height 99cm (39 in).
Width (across feet) 47 cm (18 ½ in).

This magnificent pair of torchères is a remarkable example of the high standard of carving and design produced in Wurzburg in the first quarter of the 18th century. During this period, Wurzburg, along with Ansbach, rapidly became the most important centres for early rococo furniture in Germany. Under the patronage of the counts of Schonborn, Prince-Bishops of Wurzburg, the town gained a reputation for artistic excellence that was centred around the celebrated *Residenz*, a late baroque masterpiece built by Neumann.

The style of furniture in Wurzburg took its lead from Johann Phillipp von Schonborn, Prince-Bishop from 1719 to 1729, whose taste for Parisian design was shown by the fact that he employed French craftsmen to furnish the *Residenz*. Unlike

the Court craftsmen, these Parisians did not work exclusively for the Prince-Bishop, and some rare examples of a very high standard have survived, such as these torchères, which incorporate strong naturalistic rococo forms, whilst retaining earlier baroque elements. It is this rich combination that typifies Wurzburg furniture.

Mallett,
141 New Bond Street,
London W1Y 0BS
Tel: 0171-499 7411
Fax: 0171-495 3179

One from a set of six George III mahogany open armchairs in the French manner, of superb quality and line, and with gadroon-carved frames, attributed to John Cobb. English, circa 1770.
Height 90 cm (35 ½ in).
Width 61 cm (24 in).
Depth 53 cm (21 in).

The lightness and elegance of this form of chair is clearly derived from the French *fauteuil*, with its slender cabriole legs, serpentine rails, and separated seat and back. The emphasis on its rich mahogany and the idiosyncratic, tightly gadrooned edging (a feature normally found on silver) is, however, unmistakably English. The extremely fine carving, sophisticated design and French inspiration of these chairs can be attributed to the workshop of John Cobb. Cobb, who had worked with William Vile up until 1765, had his workshops in St Martins Lane, and was regarded as the most successful interpreter of the French style. In the 1770s, Cobb supplied a suite of six of these chairs and a matching settee to Philip Yorke for Erdigg, near Wrexham, where it may be seen to this day.

Galerie Neuse Kunsthandel,
Contrescarpe 14,
28203 Bremen,
Germany
Tel: 49-421 32 56 42
Fax: 49-421 32 86 11

An important German ormolu-mounted mahogany library desk with cabinet, by David Roentgen (Herrnhaag 1743-1807 Wiesbaden).
Neuwied 1780-1795.
Height 113.5 cm (44 3/4 in).
Length (open) 166 cm (65 1/4 in).

Length (closed) 114 cm (44 7/8 in).
Depth (open) 85 cm (33 1/2 in).
Depth (closed) 61 cm (24 in).
Literature: Hans Huth, *Abraham und David Roentgen und ihre Neuwieder Möbelwerkstatt*, Berlin, 1928.

This is typical of the furniture made by David Roentgen late in his career. An identical piece, formerly in Pavlovsk Palace, St Petersburg, is now in the Bayerische Nationalmuseum, Munich.

**Pelham Galleries Ltd.,
24 & 25 Mount Street,
London W1Y 5RB
Tel: 0171-629 0905
Fax: 0171-495 4511**

A very fine and rare set of six Piedmontese rococo chairs, the serpentine backs and seats bearing the original *gros point* covers, decorated with flowers and foliage in green, pink, and blue, on a yellow ground, the finely shaped seat rails and cabriole legs decorated in yellow lacquer with *mecca*-gilded mouldings. Circa 1755.
Height 102 cm (40 in).
Width 33 cm (21 ¹/₂ in).
Depth 44.5 cm (17 ¹/₂ in).
Height of seat 44.5 cm (17 ¹/₂ in).
Literature: *Museo dell' Arredamento/Stupinigi…* a cura di Noemi Gabrielli, Tommaso Musolini Editore, Torino, fig. 128 & 148.
Mostra del Barocco Piemontese. Città Di Torino, 1963, vol. III, fig. 158 & 173b.

These chairs are among the finest examples of Torinese seat furniture of the 18th century. The use of a matching yellow palette for both frames and covers is characteristic of the brilliant colour schemes employed in the grand Torinese palaces of the period. Similar seat furniture is to be found at both the Palazzo Reale and the hunting lodge of Stupinigi. The present set, when acquired by the Pelham Galleries, had never been re-upholstered and, in restoring the chairs, the original webbing has been saved and incorporated into the upholstery.

**Pelham Galleries Ltd.,
24 & 25 Mount Street,
London W1Y 5RB
Tel: 0171-629 0905
Fax: 0171-495 4511**

A rare and highly important pair of George II giltwood pier glasses, the original mercurial bevelled plates of unusual size, each contained within a richly ornamented frame, the cresting modelled with bold C-scrolls embellished with garlands of flowers, surmounted by a leafy pagoda roof, and flanked by fluted vases of flowers supported on rococo brackets, the sides comprising scrolls and foliage emerging from fantastic architectural elements flanked by boldly modelled trees with eagles in the branches, the open-work apron flanked by rock-work and icicles. Circa 1750.
Height 275 cm (108 in).
Width 110.5 cm (43 ½ in).

These mirrors are among the finest English rococo mirrors of the mid 18th century. The mercurial bevelled plates are of very rare size, being six feet high (183 cm). This feature is an important determinant in the design as it obviates the require- ment for ornament to conceal the joint between two plates, which is usually necessary in mirrors of this scale. Indeed, virtually all published designs for large pier glasses of this period take double or multiple plates into account. The weight and uncommon boldness of the ornament suggest the earliest phase of English rococo design and a date of man- ufacture perhaps as early as the late 1740s. The design cannot be immediately associated with any specific engraving, but it is almost certain that the mirrors pre-date the publication of Chippendale's *Director* in 1754, by which time robustness had given way to a certain etiolation that became even more pronounced in the late 1750s and early 1760s. The use of tree motifs with birds, familiar in the work of both Thomas Johnson and Chippendale, and later in the work of John Linnell, is here found in its most vigorous early manifestation, the trunks mod- elled in the round and rich foliage projecting forward and outwards from the frames.

**Pelham Galleries Ltd.,
24 & 25 Mount Street,
London W1Y 5RB
Tel: 0171-629 0905
Fax: 0171-495 4511**

An outstanding George III painted papier-mâché tray by Henry Clay, the design of the polychrome decoration attributed to Michelangelo Pergolesi (fl. circa 1760 - 1801), comprising a central oval oculus decorated with clouds at sunset, surrounded by architectural compartments decorated in Etruscan taste, including four circular vignettes,

one with Pliny's doves, two each with the Arch of Titus, the fourth image of ducks on a river bank in the manner of Roman mosaic, the architectural compartments decorated with sphinxes, gryphons, birds, vases and sundry *grottesche* ornaments between a trailing border of scrolls and foliage on a lilac ground, the rim decorated with husks and trailing vines on a blue ground.
Circa 1780.
78 x 59.5 cm (30 ³/₄ x 23 ¹/₂ in).

This tray, together with another example in the Birmingham

Museum which is of identical form, painted by the same hand and stamped by Clay, is among the most elaborate and perfect examples of Italian taste in English decorative arts of the late 18th century. Interestingly, the closest parallel in European decoration is to be found in the exquisite neo-classical fans painted in Rome. It is not known whether Michelangelo Pergolesi worked in collaboration with Henry Clay, but both this tray and the Birmingham tray are very closely related to his style. Pergolesi came to England at Robert Adam's

invitation before 1770, and was extensively employed as a decorative artist. It is recorded that both Clay and Pergolesi attracted commissions from several of Adam's major clients including the Duke of Northumberland, to whom Pergolesi dedicated twelve of the fourteen parts of his *Designs for various ornaments* (1777 - 1801). Given the extraordinary quality and purely Italian style of decoration of these trays, it is not unreasonable to suggest that Pergolesi supplied the designs and may indeed have executed the decoration himself.

David Pettifer,
219 Kings Road,
Chelsea,
London SW3 5EJ
Tel. and Fax: 0171-352 3088

A rare early 19th-century Gothic pollard-oak pentagonal centre table. English, circa 1835.

Height 76 cm (30 in).
Width 137 cm (54 in).

The rarity of this piece lies in its five-sided shape and corresponding interlocking triangular stretchers.

The Gothic revival in the early 19th century witnessed the construction of several monumental Gothic mansions, many of which have since perished. This pentagonal table was probably made for a particular position in one of these buildings, maybe with one side against a narrow wall between doors, or perhaps as an unusual centre table.

The segmented top stands on five pentagonal columns joined by a mathematically intriguing stretcher. The skilful use of contrasting ebony mouldings points to the work of a sophisticated cabinetmaker.

An important pair of late
18th-century mahogany globe
stands of unusual design, fitted with
21 inch globes; by J. & W. Cary,
181 Strand, London.
Terrestrial globe dated
'March 1st 1806'.
Celestial globe dated 'Mar. 1 1799'.
Height 122 cm (48 in).
Diameter 67 cm (26 ½ in).
Globe diameter 53.5 cm (21 in).

**Ronald Phillips Ltd.,
26 Bruton Street,
London W1X 8LH
Tel: 0171-493 2341
Fax: 0171-495 0843**

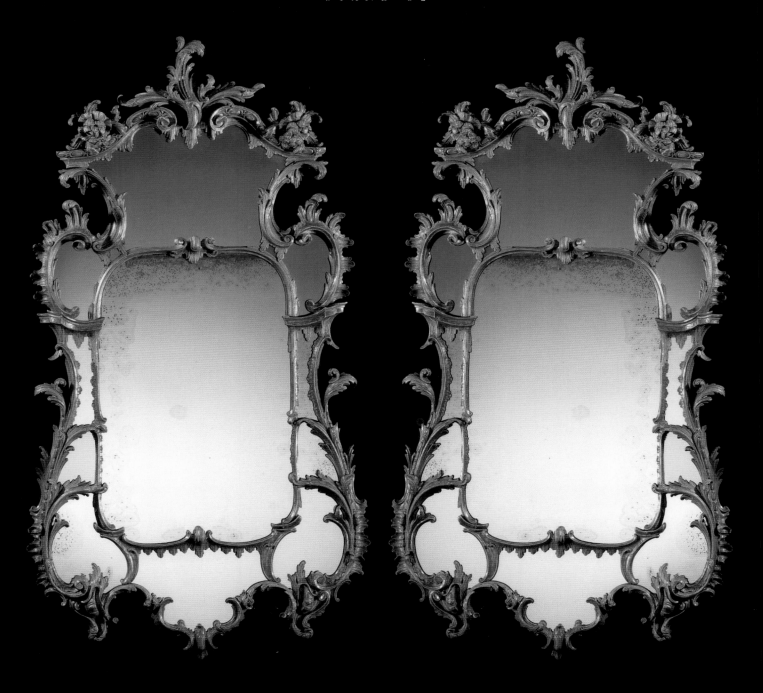

Ronald Phillips Ltd.,
26 Bruton Street,
London W1X 8LH
Tel: 0171-493 2341
Fax: 0171-495 0843

A superb pair of mid 18th-century
Chippendale period carved
giltwood border-glass mirrors
in the manner of Linnell.
Circa 1765.
Height 136 cm (53 ¹/₂ in).
Width 71 cm (28 in).

Ronald Phillips Ltd.,
26 Bruton Street,
London W1X 8LH
Tel: 0171-493 2341
Fax: 0171-495 0843

An important early 19th-century Regency mahogany partners' pedestal desk with three drawers in the frieze on each side and cupboards beneath, enclosing drawers on one side and shelves on the other. Circa 1810.
Height 81 cm (32 in).
Length 157.5 cm (62 in).
Depth 77.5 cm (30 ½ in).

**Ronald Phillips Ltd.,
26 Bruton Street,
London W1X 8LH
Tel: 0171-493 2341
Fax: 0171-495 0843**

One of a rare pair of early
19th-century Regency painted
and gilt elbow chairs in the
manner of George Smith.
Circa 1810.
Height of chair 86 cm (34 in).
Height of seat 47 cm (18½ in).
Width 56 cm (22 in).
Depth 54.5 cm (21½ in).

**Antony Preston Antiques Ltd.,
The Square,
Stow-on-the-Wold,
Gloucestershire
GL54 1AB
Tel: 01451-831586
Fax: 0171-581 5076**

A Regency rosewood cheveret in the manner of John Maclean, with applied gilt-metal mounts and pierced brass gallery. The removable four-drawer superstructure is surmounted by a graceful, turned-brass carrying handle. English, circa 1810.
Height 122 cm (48 in).
Width 66 cm (26 in).

The firm of John Maclean of Marylebone Street, established in 1770, specialised in 'Elegant Parisien Furniture', and was recommended by Sheraton, in his Dictionary of 1803, for his pieces made 'in the neatest manner'.

A cabinet, designed by Maclean, is exhibited in the Victoria and Albert Museum, displaying the same Englishness of form with distinct French overtones in its high quality gilded brass mounts, and brass mouldings to outline the drawers.

The taste for French furniture in England remained undiminished by the Napoleonic Wars. The restoration of the Bourbon monarchy in 1814 heralded the resurgence of pre-Revolutionary styles, giving further inspiration to English cabinetmakers, already in the grip of 'L'Empire'. The Prince Regent's taste for French works of art fuelled the fashion to which John Maclean's highly skilled workshop responded.

**Antony Preston Antiques Ltd.,
The Square,
Stow-on-the-Wold,
Gloucestershire
GL54 1AB
Tel: 01451-831586
Fax: 0171-581 5076**

A William and Mary double-domed bureau cabinet in superbly patinated walnut, the bureau with shaped, stepped interior and a well. The doors, with engraved mirror plates, enclose a fitted upperpart with candle slides below. English, circa 1700. Height 229 cm (90 in). Width 104 cm (41 in).

The arrival of William and Mary from Holland in 1688 marked the beginning of an era of peace and prosperity in England. The loftier rooms typical of this period led to a demand for taller pieces of furniture that were required to be functional as well as elegant. The bureau cabinet fulfilled these criteria, creating ample scope for the cabinet-maker's art, whilst providing a practical writing surface coupled with generous storage. The mirror doors of the upper section reflected light from candlesticks positioned on the candle slides, at once illuminating the room and the scribe's papers.

The influx of skilled craftsmen from the continent happily coincided with a supply of native walnut. It was a material well-suited to the more advanced techniques of veneering, applied mouldings, and crossbanding, and is seen here in all its splendid depth of colour and patination.

Brian Rolleston Ltd.,
104A Kensington Church St,
London W8 4BU
Tel. and Fax: 0171-229 5892

A Queen Anne walnut wing
chair. Circa 1710.
Height 114 cm (45 in).
Width 86 cm (34 in).

During the early 18th century,
upholstered furniture became
much more comfortable and the
wing chair, which had existed
towards the end of the 17th
century, achieved its most pleas-
ing and satisfactory shape.

This chair, in
English walnut,
illustrates these
features and incor-
porates a carved
shell on the knee,
which is typical of
fine examples of
this period.

Brian Rolleston Ltd.,
104A Kensington Church St,
London W8 4BU
Tel. and Fax: 0171-229 5892

A George I walnut tallboy.
Circa 1720.
Height 183 cm (72 in).
Width 104 cm (41 in).
Depth 56 cm (22 in).

The growing prosperity in England during the early 18th century is reflected in the furniture used for the storing of linen and clothes.

Throughout the 18th century, chest-on-chests, or tallboys, were popular items, and this is a fine, well-proportioned example, dating from the beginning of this period. It is executed in well-figured walnut and retains its original engraved handles and escutcheons.

Stair & Company Ltd.,
14 Mount Street,
London W1Y 5RA
Tel: 0171-499 1784
Fax: 0171-629 1050

A fine George III mahogany commode of serpentine shape with hipped corners, enclosing three drawers with figured veneers to the front. The base has a fluted frieze, above four turned and fluted legs which terminate in castors. Excellent colour and figure to the top. English, circa 1775.
Height 88 cm (34 in).
Width 99 cm (39 in).

Depth 58 cm (23 in).

The design of this unusual piece is most closely associated with the designs of William and John Linnell.

Stair & Company Ltd.,
14 Mount Street,
London W1Y 5RA
Tel: 0171-499 1784
Fax: 0171-629 1050

A superbly carved George II giltwood side table with a veneered marble top. The frieze has an elegant guilloche-carved border and a central carved double scallop-shell flanked by leafy sprays. The side friezes are similarly decorated with acanthus leaves to the knees of the legs, which terminate in bold hairy paw feet. English, circa 1745.

Height 89 cm (35 in).
Width 122 cm (61 in).
Depth 61 cm (24 in).

STAIR & COMPANY LTD

**Stair & Company Ltd.,
14 Mount Street,
London W1Y 5RA
Tel: 0171-499 1784
Fax: 0171-629 1050**

An extremely rare George III Pembroke table with beautifully figured veneers of harewood, inlaid on the top with central oval medallions of amboyna, which is also applied to the corners of the rising panels, and with boxwood bandings inlaid with dots of amboyna. One panel is hinged, opening to reveal a fitted work-box interior; the other, operated by a mechanism, forms the top of a writing casket with four drawers fitted for painting, sketching, and writing, its outer surfaces veneered with satinwood inlaid with amboyna ovals. Both flaps have central oval medallions of laburnum oyster veneer, linked to a necklace motif which is echoed in the inlay across the drawer fronts, and in the friezes of the ends. The table rests on square tapering legs, decorated with stringing, and ending in castors. English, circa 1785.

Height 72 cm (28 ½ in).
Width 83 cm (33 in).
Depth 62 cm (24 ½ in).

This is one of a small number of tables with similar decoration that must have been produced to order. Another example, from the Avray Tipping Collection, is in the Bowes Museum.

O.F. Wilson Ltd.,
Queen's Elm Parade,
Old Church Street,
Chelsea,
London SW3 6EJ
Tel: 0171-352 9554
Fax: 0171-351 0765

A Louis XVI period commode in well-figured mahogany with original brass mounts and marble top.
Height 87.6 cm (34 ½ in).
Width 123.2 cm (48 ½ in).
Depth 56.5 cm (22 ¼ in).

O.F. Wilson Ltd.,
Queen's Elm Parade,
Old Church Street,
Chelsea,
London SW3 6EJ
Tel: 0171-352 9554
Fax: 0171-351 0765

A pair of hall benches in oak,
attributed to George Bullock, the
tapered seats with turned arms
and on turned reeded legs. 1817.
Length 121.9 cm (48 in).

O.F. Wilson Ltd.,
Queen's Elm Parade,
Old Church Street,
Chelsea,
London SW3 6EJ
Tel: 0171-352 9554
Fax: 0171-351 0765

A fine and rare English
mantelpiece in white marble,
well-carved with entwined hops
and hop leaves, 1820, shown with
an English, late 18th-century
polished steel fire-grate, circa
1790, beneath a Louis XVI
period carved giltwood mirror
with original plate, 1770.
Height (mantelpiece)
124 cm (49 in).
Width 162.5 cm (64 in).
Height (mirror) 172.7 cm (68 in).
Width 109.2 cm (43 in).

Witney Antiques,
96-100 Corn Street,
Witney,
Oxfordshire
OX8 7BU
Tel: 01993-703902
Fax: 01993-779852

An important and rare mahogany armchair of exceptional size on four cabriole legs, with outswept arms and shaped cresting rail. English, circa 1740.
Height 99 cm (39 in).
Width 81 cm (32 in).

Armchairs like this are uncommon and generally of smaller size. This example, with its turned spindles and solid seat, shares some of the constructional characteristics of the Windsor chair. However, the Windsor chair is associated with rural areas, and the usual timbers used were ash, yew, elm, and fruit-woods. The use of walnut and mahogany was much less common, and is associated with the grandest examples. The quality of construction of this chair, with its massive seat with carved scroll detail, and its beautifully drawn cabriole legs, suggests a major cabinetmaker of the period.

Witney Antiques,
96-100 Corn Street,
Witney,
Oxfordshire
OX8 7BU
Tel: 01993-703902
Fax: 01993-779852

A fine small walnut gate-leg table, an exceptional broad-rim pewter charger, and one of a pair of outstanding joined oak backstools. English, second half of the 17th century.
Height (chair) 95 cm (37 ½ in).

Oak was the primary wood used in the manufacture of furniture during the greater part of the 17th century, although walnut, both solid and as veneer, was increasingly used towards the end of this period. During the 17th century, the backstool became an important item in prosperous households as a more comfortable alternative to the stool. It often shows design details that were fashionable at the time it

was made. Backstools were constructed in many regions of Britain, and their decoration is often specific to their origins. This fact contributes significantly to the study of regional furniture manufacture and its develop-

ment. This backstool and its pair were almost certainly made in Yorkshire, and they show distinct differences from those made in Lancashire, Derbyshire and other regions of northern England.

**Clifford Wright Antiques Ltd.,
104 & 106 Fulham Road,
London SW3 6HS
Tel: 0171-589 0986
Fax: 0171-589 3565**

A fine, late George III, Adam-period, semi-elliptical giltwood console, retaining the original marble with sienna inlay. Circa 1780. Height 98 cm (38 ½ in). Width 145 cm (57 in). Depth 72.5 cm (28 ½ in).

In the same year that Thomas Chippendale's *Director* was published, 1754, the young Robert Adam arrived in Italy to complete his studies as an architect. He was to develop a style completely opposed to that illustrated in the *Director*, and to become, in his turn, an inspiration to many designers of the third quarter of the 18th century. (Praise was not, however, unanimous. Horace Walpole was heard to mutter disdainfully of Mr Adams' work, 'Gingerbread and sippets of embroidery'.)

This pier table is a fine example of the period, with its original white marble inlaid with sienna, over a frieze of finely carved anthemions, supported on robust reeded legs joined by a stretcher.

**Clifford Wright Antiques Ltd.,
104 & 106 Fulham Road,
London SW3 6HS
Tel: 0171-589 0986
Fax: 0171-589 3565**

A superb Regency bonheur-du-jour with writing slide, circa 1810. Height 126 cm (49 ½ in). Width 94 cm (37 in). Depth 44.5 cm (17 ½ in).

This elegant, galleried writing table with tambour slide embodies much that was held in high regard during the Regency period. Constructed in rosewood with a wealth of brass and ormolu ornament, it also includes a convex mirror, in the latest fashion of the time. The overall design reflects its relationship with earlier French examples.

ORIENTAL CERAMICS, FURNITURE AND WORKS OF ART

*Detail of a carved ivory cabinet, circa 1650, from Sri Lanka.
Spink & Son Ltd*

*A Chinese pottery figure of a tomb guardian, Tang dynasty (618-907 AD).
Vanderven & Vanderven Oriental Art*

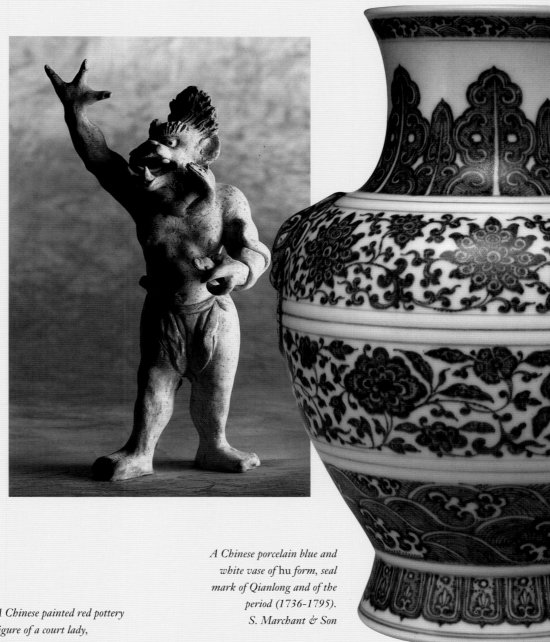

*A Chinese painted red pottery figure of a court lady,
Tang dynasty (618-907 AD).
Spink & Son Ltd*

A Chinese porcelain blue and white vase of hu *form, seal mark of Qianlong and of the period (1736-1795).
S. Marchant & Son*

Michael Goedhuis,
116 Mount Street,
London W1Y 5HD
Tel: 0171-629 2228
Fax: 0171-409 3338

A parcel-gilt bronze horse and rider. China, Qing dynasty, 18th century.
Height 29.5 cm (11 ¼ in).

This beautifully cast sculpture probably represents a polo player. Large Qing dynasty non-Buddhist parcel-gilt bronze sculptures are rare. This may be compared with a detailed figure of Liu Hai in Beudeley, *The Chinese Collector through the Centuries*, no. 130.

Michael Goedhuis,
116 Mount Street,
London W1Y 5HD
Tel: 0171-629 2228
Fax: 0171-409 3338

Autumn Sunshine by Yang Yanping. 1996. Coloured ink on rice paper. 91 x 161 cm (35 ³/₄ x 63 ¹/₂ in).

The leading painter of her generation in China and, since 1986, in the United States, Yang Yanping combines a faultless mastery of Chinese classical technique with a free and spontaneous modern vision. Established in many of the leading museums in the West, she remains restlessly audacious and continues to surprise with her distinctive balance of East and West.

Luís Alegria,
Av. Dr Antunes Guimarães 142,
4100 Porto,
Portugal
Tel: 351-2 6182324
Fax: 351-2 6105446

A pair of Chinese export porcelain vases and covers decorated in *famille verte* enamels, Kangxi period (1662-1722). Height 45 cm (17 ¾ in).

Grosvenor Antiques Ltd.,
27 Holland Street,
Kensington,
London W8 4NA
Tel: 0171-937 8649
Fax: 0171-937 7179

One of a very rare set of twelve Chinese watercolours of baskets of flowers, painted on pith paper. Canton, circa 1840. The original brocade-covered album bears the studio mark in red, 'Youqua. Painter. Old St. No. 34'. 18 x 25 cm (9 x 7 in).

Openwork baskets of flowers were customarily given to celebrate marriages, births, birthdays and other happy family occasions.

Around 1750, Chinese artists began to produce works of art specifically for the expanding European market. These were conveyed home in the East India Company ships of the European maritime nations.

In the early 19th century, rice paper came into use, so called because of its translucent qualities. It was, in fact, made from the pith of *Tetrapanex papyfera*, a native plant of China. White pigment was used to heighten the effect, and areas on the reverse were also blocked out in white, giving an appearance of relief.

All facets of Chinese life, including the flora, fauna, costumes, and trades, were portrayed and sent to Europe. By 1830, Canton had over 30 painting shops or studios employing some 3,000 artists.

**Robert Hall,
15c Clifford Street,
London W1X 1RF
Tel: 0171-734 4008
Fax: 0171-734 4408**

Left, An 18th-century ivory snuff bottle of rounded form on a raised foot, the undecorated body with a fine patination, the stopper of coral on a turquoise collar. Height 5.5 cm (2 ⅛ in). Provenance: Lionel Copley . Literature: Robert Hall, *Chinese Snuff Bottles VI from the collection of Lionel Copley*, Part I, no. 5.

Chinese snuff bottles, and the powdered tobacco they contained, were at the heart of a fashion which had no equivalent in China's long history. As the craze for taking snuff increased, so too did the quest for exotic materials for the creation of bottles. This resulted in every material known to the Chinese being used – glass, porcelain, jade and other hard-stones, ivory, coral, lacquer, bamboo, amber, etc.

Great elegance of form was often attained by the makers of snuff bottles in materials that

were allowed to speak for themselves, without further decoration. Plain, undecorated ivory bottles are very rare, and the evenly patinated, creamy-yellow colour of this one is the result of many years of fondling and use.

Right, A turquoise snuff bottle of natural pebble form, the green colour suffused with a network of darker lines, the stopper of coral carved in twig form.
1780 - 1850.
Height 5.4 cm (2 ⅛ in).
Provenance: Charles Cox .

Turquoise is a relatively soft stone, and is ideally suited to the Chinese aesthetic of subtle and natural transformation through use. The stone absorbs natural oils from the hand and these gradually mellow the often bright, rather harsh, original-colour to gently varying shades of blue and green.

Robert Hall,
15c Clifford Street,
London W1X 1RF
Tel: 0171-734 4008
Fax: 0171-734 4408

Left, An amber snuff bottle of even, transparent, golden-brown colour, undecorated and extremely well-hollowed, the stopper of pink tourmaline on a stained walrus-ivory mount. 1750 - 1850.
Height 6.5 cm (2 ¹/₂ in).

Amber is the fossilized resin of coniferous trees, and colours range from rich mahogany red to a bright opaque yellow. It is a soft substance, despite being a fossil, and as it takes a superb surface patina, it was an ideal material for a tactile snuff bottle.

Right, A glass snuff bottle, the opaque yellow ground overlaid in translucent yellow, each side with floral sprays issuing from serrated rocks. The base is inscribed *Qianlong yuzhi* (Made by Imperial Command of the

Qianlong Emperor). The stopper is of pink tourmaline. Beijing Palace Workshops, 1736 - 1795. Height 6 cm (2 ³/₈ in).

This extremely rare bottle is one of only three known overlay-glass snuff bottles bearing the mark *Qianlong yuzhi*. A similar bottle, differing only in the type of floral motif, is illustrated in *A Congregation of Snuff Bottle Connoisseurs, An Exhibition at the Tsui Museum of Art*, no. 40, and it is likely that these bottles were made as part of a series for the

Emperor. During the Qing dynasty, an elaborate code of sumptuary laws decreed that yellow was a colour reserved solely for Imperial use, and this regulation was apparently strictly enforced until the end of the 18th century.

S. Marchant & Son,
120 Kensington Church St.,
London W8 4BH
Tel: 0171-229 5319
Fax: 0171-792 8979

A Chinese porcelain Imperial
'Hundred Deer' vase of *hu* form
with stylised dragon handles,
painted on either side in the
famille rose palette with a
continuous scene of deer
amongst mountains and trees.
Sealmark of Qianlong
and of the period,
1736 - 1795.
Height 43.6 cm (17 in).

The shape of this vase was inspired by an ancient bronze ritual vessel from the Shang dynasty (circa 1500 - 1028 BC), which, along with numerous other such forms, were copied in ceramics in the ensuing centuries. Emperors of the Qing dynasty, of whom Qianlong was the fourth, were particularly interested in ordering traditional types of works of art for the palaces. This was partly to help legitimise their hold on power by giving at least the appearance of continuity to a relatively young dynasty, which dated only from the middle of the previous century.

The principal theme of the decoration is longevity. Deer are one of the main Chinese symbols of long life, and there are many on this vase. The theme is further emphasised by the overhanging pine trees, flowering peach plants, and *lingzhi* fungus, all of which have a similar meaning. In Chinese thought, the high mountains have auspicious significance and the dragon handles represent the Emperor himself.

A similar piece in the Shanghai Museum is illustrated in *Chugoku Toji Zenshu*, vol. 21, pl. 103, and another, from the Grandidier Collection in the Musée Guimet, is illustrated in *Oriental Ceramics, The World's Great Collections*, vol. 7, no. 190.

S. Marchant & Son,
120 Kensington Church St.,
London W8 4BH
Tel: 0171-229 5319
Fax: 0171-792 8979

A Chinese Ming porcelain yellow-ground gourd vase decorated in underglaze blue and iron-red on the upper and lower sections with flowers and scrolling foliage divided by a band of prunus flowers, the foot with a band of stylised scrolls and lappets.
Jiajing six-character mark in underglaze blue within a double ring and of the period, 1522 - 1566.
Height 21.5 cm (8 ½ in).

Provenance: The collection of Stephen Junkunc, III.
Literature: *Oriental Ceramics, The World's Great Collections,* vol. 6, no. 41, for a smaller example in the Percival David Foundation.

Spink & Son Ltd.,
5 King Street,
St James's,
London SW1Y 6QS
Tel: 0171-930 7888
Fax: 0171-839 4853

A pair of rare pierced gilt-bronze figures of elephants, inset with semi-precious stones.
Chinese, 18th century.
Height 26 cm (10 ¼ in).
Width 30.5 cm (12 in).

The elephant is an archetype of strength, intelligence and wisdom, and possesses symbolic qualities. The image of the elephant has powerful Buddhist connotations: it is the steed of the Bodhisattva Samatbhadra, and Siddartha was miraculously conceived when his mother, Queen Maya, dreamt that he entered her womb as a beautiful, small, white elephant.

By the time of the Emperor Qianlong (1736-1796), images of elephants had become fashionable. The Emperor was a prodigious patron of the arts, and under his rule, China prospered from the trade with the Western world – a trade which stimulated demand for works of quality.

Sculptures of elephants can be found in a range of media, including ivory and porcelain, though the finest are often of cloisonné. They were sometimes modelled with upper vases which could be used to hold significant objects, such as carved ivory *lingzhi*-fungus, which evoked the idea of immortality. Porcelain models appeared at the end of the 18th century, sharing a similar design to the cloisonné originals, and the fashion for this style of elephant soon spread to the West, through the China Trade.

Spink & Son Ltd.,
5 King Street,
St James's,
London SW1Y 6QS
Tel: 0171-930 7888
Fax: 0171-839 4853

A fine gilt bronze figure of a Bodhisattva. Chinese, Yongle period (1403 - 1424). Height 21 cm (8 ½ in).

This gilt bronze figure of a Bodhisattva represents the fine tradition of metal sculptures cast during the Yongle period (1403 - 1424), early in the Ming dynasty (1368 - 1644).

During the previous Yuan dynasty (1279 - 1368), Lamaist images had taken their inspiration from contemporary Tibetan and Nepalese styles, the religion having entered China after the Mongol invasion.

Craftsmen continued to work in the Imperial workshops during the early Ming dynasty and though the Tibetan hold was still very strong, the images clearly began to show more Chinese influence. Though made mainly for Lamaist temples and monasteries, the decoration became unencumbered and uncluttered in its presentation, the facial features conforming more to Chinese taste, the robes without inset precious stones, and the lotus petals narrower than in subsequent eras.

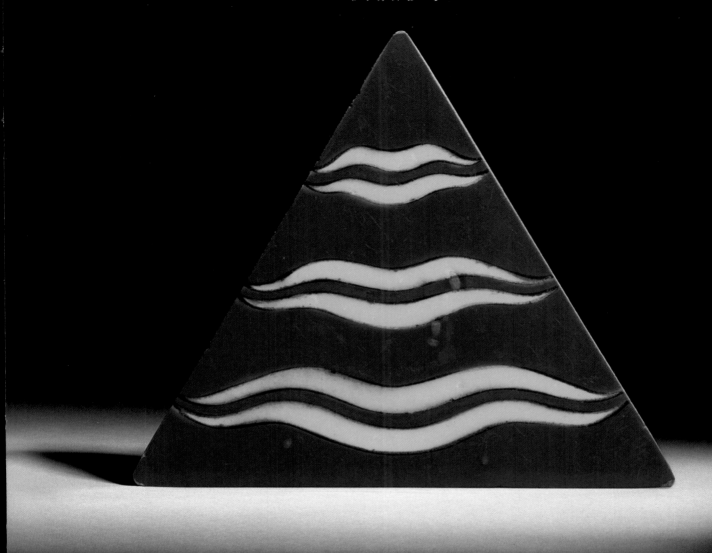

Spink & Son Ltd.,
5 King Street,
St James's,
London SW1Y 6QS
Tel: 0171-930 7888
Fax: 0171-839 4853

A set of six triangular ceramic tiles from Turkey, each decorated with three graduating 'cloud-bands', also called 'tiger-stripes' or 'Buddha-lips', painted in lapis-blue and ochre-yellow outlined in black. Turkish (Kütahya), late 18th - early 19th century.

Each tile 16 x 18 cm (6 ½ x 7 in). Entire panel 16 x 66.5 cm (26 ½ in).

After the demise of the Iznik workshops in the 17th century, pottery continued to be produced in Turkey at Kütahya, a town on the edge of the Anatolian plateau, about twenty kilometres to the south-east of Istanbul.

Typical of Kütahya-ware are small bowls, plates, and jugs, either in blue and white, or in a colourful palette including yellow and green, showing the influence of Japanese Kakiemon porcelain.

On the whole, Kütahya tiles lacked the distinction and technical finesse of their Iznik predecessors. However, there are exceptions including the famous group of Kaaba pictures (found in mosques, *masjids* (prayer halls) and various museums), and tiles such as these. The unusual triangular shape and vibrant colouring of the latter surely aligns them with the very finest offerings of the celebrated Iznik tradition.

The tiles are painted in the lapis-blue and ochre-yellow underglaze characteristic of Kütahya. Although these colours were typical of this area it is nonetheless rare to find them applied with such startling intensity. The 'cloud-band' or 'Buddha-lips' design illustrated here is thought to have originated from central Asia. Increasingly popular in Eastern decorative arts, this motif, also known as 'tiger-stripes', was particularly prolific in the Ottoman period and found expression on ceramics and textiles.

**Vanderven & Vanderven
Oriental Art,
Peperstraat 6,
5211 KM 's-Hertogenbosch,
The Netherlands
Tel: 31-73 6146251
Fax: 31-73 6130662**

A very fine gilt bronze standing figure of Avalokitesvara as 'the luck of Yunnan', the face with serene expression, the eyes narrowed, the hair dressed in *jatamukuta* and set with a small figure of the Amitabha Buddha. The left hand is in the *vitarka-mudra*, the naked torso and head adorned with jewellery, and the folded skirt elaborately knotted around the waist.
China, Yunnan, Dali Kingdom, Song dynasty (960 - 1127), circa 11th - 12th century.
Height 29.5 cm (11 ⅝ in).
Provenance: Dutch private collection.
Literature: *Arts from the rooftop of Asia*, The Metropolitan Museum of Art, New York, April 1971, no. 90. *Der Tempel der Drei Pagoden von Dali*, Albert Lutz Museum Rietberg, Zurich, 1991, p. 122-127.

An estimated fifteen figures like this are known in the world, most of them in museums in the United States (the Freer Gallery, Washington, the Boston Museum of Fine Arts, the San Diego Museum of Art, and the Asian Art Museum, San Francisco, as well as the British Museum, London). All are of a single type, representing the Bodhisattva Avalokitesvara. Until the remarkable article by Helen Chapin was published in 1944, these rare bronzes were labelled Chinese (Wei, Tang or Song period), Siamese, Nepalese, Tibetan, or even Bengalese. On the basis of a scroll painting commissioned during the 12th century, Chapin established that the majority of the known bronze images were cast in the semi-independent Kingdom of Nanzhao (Yunnan), which flourished under the Duan dynasty (649 - 1253).

VANDERVEN & VANDERVEN ORIENTAL ART

**Vanderven & Vanderven
Oriental Art,
Peperstraat 6,
5211 KM 's-Hertogenbosch,
The Netherlands
Tel: 31-73 6146251
Fax: 31-73 6130662**

A pair of large Chinese blue and white porcelain rouleau vases, Kangxi period (1662-1722). Height 74.5 and 75.5 cm (29 3/8 and 29 3/4 in)

The long reign of the Emperor Kangxi (1662-1722) saw the beginning of a period that might be considered the golden age of Qing porcelains: with the arrival of Tsa'ng Ying-hsuan as director of the Imperial factory at Ching-te Chen (1681 or 1683), a brilliant new chapter in the history of the potter's art began. Spanning a period of 60 years, Kangxi porcelains embrace several changes in style. Generally speaking, the robust character of the late Transition period wares made before 1683 gives way to the elegant opulence of the middle Kangxi period, and then to the more refined and quieter taste of the later porcelains that foreshadow the delicate style of the Yongzheng period.

This pair of vases clearly belongs to the middle Kangxi period. Nature, so important in Chinese culture, dominates the detailed painting on the large cylindrical surface. The whole makes strong reference to scroll-painting, which plays a significant role in Chinese art.

Grace Wu Bruce,
701 Universal Trade Centre,
3 Arbuthnot Road,
Hong Kong
Tel: 852-2537 1288
Fax: 852-2537 0213

A continuous horseshoe arm-chair, of *huanghuali* wood. Chinese, 17th century. Height 94 cm (37 in).

Width 59.2 cm (23 ¼ in). Depth 45.5 cm (18 in). Literature: Curtis Evarts, 'Classical Chinese Furniture in the Piccus Collection', *Journal of the Classical Chinese Furniture Society*, Autumn 1992, p.15. Sherman Lee, 'Chinese Domestic Furniture', *The Bulletin of The Cleveland Museum of Art*, Cleveland Ohio, March 1957.

This is an example of a rare type of horseshoe armchair, where the arms do not protrude beyond the posts but continue down the seat to become the legs. Such chairs are much more unusual than those where the arms do protrude.

There is a completely plain example in the collection of the Cleveland Museum of Art (Lee,

op. cit.) with pillar-shaped struts instead of the openwork round struts found on this chair.

The present chair may be compared to a similar piece in a private collection in Hong Kong (Evarts op. cit.) which has pillar-shaped struts and a carved, coiled dragon in the back splat medallion, instead of the *fangding* shown here.

Grace Wu Bruce,
701 Universal Trade Centre,
3 Arbuthnot Road,
Hong Kong
Tel: 852-2537 1288
Fax: 852-2537 0213

A *huanghuali* wood *qiaotouan* table. Chinese, late 16th to early 17th century.
Height 83.4 cm (32 ³/₄ in).
Width 179 cm (70 ¹/₂ in).
Depth 41.6 cm (16 ³/₈ in).
Literature: Wu Bruce, *Chinese Classical Furniture*, Hong Kong, 1995, pl. 12. Wang Shixiang, *Connoisseurship of Chinese Furniture: Ming and Early Qing Dynasties*, Hong Kong, 1990, p.100. Wang Shixiang, *Classic Chinese Furniture: Ming and Early Qing Dynasties*, London, 1986, p. 158-159.

Tables like this with everted ends and recessed legs belong to a classic type in Ming furniture design. This table may be compared to a similar example with carved spandrels and aprons illustrated in Wang Shixiang, *Connoisseurship of Chinese Furniture*, (op. cit.) and another piece with angular spandrels and straight apron in Wang Shixiang, *Classic Chinese Furniture* (op. cit.).

Grace Wu Bruce,
701 Universal Trade Centre,
3 Arbuthnot Road,
Hong Kong
Tel: 852-2537 1288
Fax: 852-2537 0213

A small *huanghuali* wood *ping-touan* side table. Chinese, late 16th to early 17th century. Height 75.4 cm (29 ⁵/₈ in). Width 88.7 cm (35 in). Depth 34.3 cm (13 ¹/₂ in). Literature: Chen Zengbi, *Zhongyang Gongyi Meishu Xueyan Yuancang: Zhenpin Tulu dier ji,* *Mingshi Jiaju*, Central Academy of Arts & Crafts: Illustrations of collections, vol. 2, Ming Furniture Beijing, 1994, p. 42. Craig Clunas, *Chinese Furniture*, London, 1988, p. 46.

This classic design has its origin in ancient Chinese architecture in wood. This table may be compared to the similar but longer piece in the collection of the Central Academy of Arts & Crafts, Beijing (Chen, op. cit.). A longer table of similar design is in the collection of the Victoria and Albert Museum, London (Clunas, op. cit.).

Grace Wu Bruce,
701 Universal Trade Centre,
3 Arbuthnot Road,
Hong Kong
Tel: 852-2537 1288
Fax: 852-2537 0213

A sloping-stile wood-hinged cabinet, of *huanghuali* and burl wood. Chinese, late 16th to early 17th century.
Height 107.8 cm (42 ¼ in).
Width 71 cm (29 in).

Depth 41 cm (16 ⅛ in).
Literature: Robert Hatfield Ellsworth, *Chinese Furniture: Hardwood Examples of the Ming and Early Ching Dynasties*, New York, 1971, p. 122. George N. Kates, *Chinese Household Furniture*, New York and London, 1948, (reprinted New York, 1971), pl. 10.

This is an example of one of the most ingenious and beautiful designs of classic Chinese furniture. The four main stiles are recessed from the corners of the top and slope gently outward in a subtle, almost imperceptible splay. This simple design feature gives the cabinet its refined elegance and a sense of balance and stability.

The doors, with extended dowels on both ends, fit into sockets in the cabinet frame members and act as hinges. This frees the cabinet from the need for applied hinges, maintaining its clean lines.

This cabinet may be compared with a closely similar piece in the Nelson-Atkins Museum of Art, Kansas City, (Ellsworth, op. cit.), and another one illustrated in Georg Kates, *Chinese Household Furniture*, (op. cit.) in the collection of Dr Gustav Ecke.

OTHER WORKS OF ART

An 18th-century English
brass sponge-dish, with
traces of original
silvering, circa 1755.
Rupert Gentle Antiques

A pair of Caribbean folk-art
figures, with much original
polychrome, circa 1850.
Alistair Sampson Antiques Ltd

il of an 18th-century
nental double-sided
r-bread mould in walnut.
E. Foster

A. & E. Foster,
Little Heysham,
Forge Road,
Naphill,
Buckinghamshire
HP14 4SU
Tel: and Fax: 01494-562024
(By appointment only)

An important oak roof boss, carved with a 'wodehouse', or wild man, and a chained lion. English, circa 1400. Diameter 30 cm (12 in).

The subject of the 'wodehouse' was very popular during the late medieval period in England. The name is derived from the Anglo-Saxon *wude wasa*, meaning wild man. He is often shown associated with a lion, whose skin he wears to illustrate his great strength and his power over animals.

English wood carving of any quality is rare from this period, as the majority of figurative work was defaced or destroyed during the Reformation. The dramatic quality of the carving and the composition within the round boss must rank this as one of the finest examples of medieval wood carving remaining from this lost-period of art history in England.

Other examples of this subject are in Chester Cathedral and Lincoln Cathedral, and also in the churches in Beverley, Yorkshire, and Norton, Suffolk.

Halcyon Days,
14 Brook Street,
London W1Y 1AA
and
4 Royal Exchange,
London EC3V 3LL
Tel: 0171-629 8811
Fax: 0171-409 0280

Three treen objects: a rare 18th-century native American carved wood powder flask surmounted with the head of a duck, circa 1780, and two snuff-boxes in animal form: the boar carved of fruitwood with bone tusks, the whimsical lion carved from two coquilla nuts, circa 1800.
Length (powder flask):
25.4 cm (10 in).
Literature: Edward H. Pinto, *Treen and other wooden bygones*, G. Bell & Sons Ltd, London, 1969.

David Pettifer,
219 Kings Road,
Chelsea,
London SW3 5EJ
Tel. and Fax: 0171-352 3088

A fine pair of Regency octagonal decorated tole tea cannisters with lids. English, circa 1820.

Height 38 cm (15 in).
Width 28 cm (11 in).
Depth 21 cm (8 ½ in).

From the 18th century, tea tins were made for retailers to show off the various blends of tea. The decoration was meant to conjure up the mystery of the Orient by imitating Chinese lacquer with its gilt decoration and exotic figures – all part of the art of salesmanship. There may have been as many as ten or twelve such tins gracing the shelves of the smartest shops.

The tins shown here are numbered one and two, and are painted Chinese red with a central figure amid foliage in the chinoiserie style. The use of green on the body of the tins and on the dress is unusual, as are the charming Chinese key-pattern borders.

Alistair Sampson Antiques Ltd.,
120 Mount Street,
London W1Y 5HB
Tel: 0171-409 1799
Fax: 0171-409 7717

A very fine George II brass kettle, stand and burner, the kettle of inverted pear shape, with secured scrolling swing handle, the bow top retaining the original plaited covering. The spout and mounts to the handle are modelled with scrolled fluting and the body is engraved on one side with the coat of arms of Perrott in a shaped cartouche with rococo mantling and the motto 'GRATITUDE'. The other side of the body bears the crest of Perrott. The stand has three scroll legs and shell feet, and is fitted with a plain burner. Circa 1750.
Height 37 cm (14 ½ in).

PAINTINGS, WATERCOLOURS, DRAWINGS AND PRINTS

A still life of flowers in a glass vase *by Jan Baptist van Fornenburgh (active 1608- 1656).* Johnny Van Haeften Ltd

Lady Alice Eleanor Louise Montague *by Giovanni Boldini (1842-1931), gouache, watercolour and crayon. Stoppenbach & Delestre Ltd*

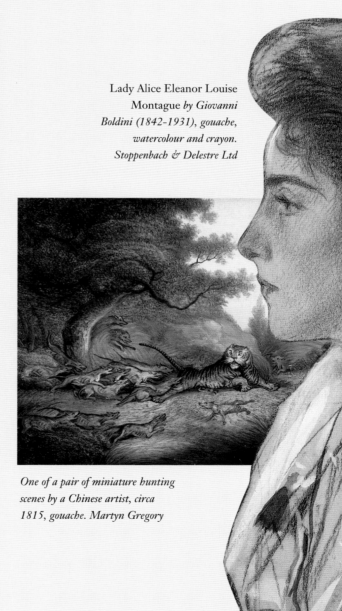

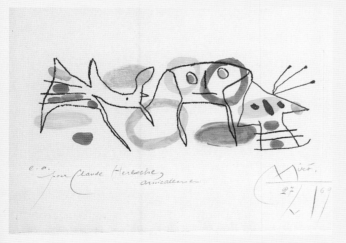

La Magie Quotidienne *by Joan Miro (1893-1953), colour etching. William Weston Gallery*

One of a pair of miniature hunting scenes by a Chinese artist, circa 1815, gouache. Martyn Gregory

ail from La Table de
*apagne by Henri Le
ner (Port-Louis 1862-
Versailles).
ard Green

Konrad O. Bernheimer Ltd.,
1 Mount Street,
Mayfair,
London W1Y 5AA
Tel: 0171-495 7028
Fax: 0171-495 7027
(By appointment only)

An Allegory of Air and Fire by Jan van Kessel the Elder (1626 - Antwerp - 1679). Oil on copper. 50.3 x 64.5 cm (19 ³/₄ x 25 ³/₈ in).

Jan van Kessel the Elder was the pupil of his uncle, (Jan) Breughel de Velours. In 1644, he became a member of the guild of St Luke in Antwerp. He married in 1647 and raised thirteen children, two of whom themselves became painters. He was a painter of landscape, flowers, fruit, birds and insects, all in the style of Breughel de Velours.

This charming, and only recently discovered, painting depicts the elements Air and Fire, and may have formed a pendant to one of Water and Earth. To the left one sees many different birds, a forge and numerous other attributes of Fire, such as arms and armour, gold coins, and an erupting volcano in the background.

Konrad O. Bernheimer Ltd.,
1 Mount Street,
Mayfair,
London W1Y 5AA
Tel: 0171-495 7028
Fax: 0171-495 7027
(By appointment only)

Hector summoning Paris to war by Angelika Kauffman RA (1741-1807). Signed and dated, 'Angelika Kauffman, R.A. / Pinx: 1770'. Oil on canvas. 145 x 121 cm (57 x 47 ½ in). Provenance: Private collection, Ireland; thence by direct descent, private collection, Germany.

Not only was Kauffman a founder-member of the Royal Academy and one of the foremost neo-classical artists of her time, she also chose to make her reputation as a history painter, a genre considered to be the highest brand of art and, at the time, out of bounds to female artists, principally because of their lack of means to acquire the necessary literary education. Training in anatomy was also a problem for women, who were not generally allowed to draw from nude models.

This painting is an excellent example of her talent as a history painter and depicts a scene from the Trojan war when Hector summons his younger brother Paris from Helen's side and orders him to join the battle against the Greeks.

Konrad O. Bernheimer Ltd.,
1 Mount Street,
Mayfair,
London W1Y 5AA
Tel: 0171-495 7028
Fax: 0171-495 7027
(By appointment only)

A still life of fruit with sunflowers
and a façon de Venise glass, all upon
a stone ledge.
Signed on the ledge, lower left,
'C DE HEEM'.
Oil on canvas.
57 x 75 cm (22 ½ x 29 ½ in).

WILLIAM DRUMMOND

**William Drummond,
(Covent Garden Gallery Ltd.),
8 St James's Chambers,
2-10 Ryder Street,
London SW1Y 6QA
Tel. and Fax: 0171-930 9696**

Writing at 7 Owens Row (in the book room) by Richard Parminter Cuff (1819-1876).
Watercolours on paper.
39.3 x 29.8 cm (15 ¹/₂ x 11 ³/₄ in).
Literature: Charlotte Gere, *Nineteenth Century Interiors*, 1992, p. 84, pl. 28. The Pierpont Morgan Library, New York, *19th Century Decoration, The Art of the Interior*, 1989, p. 265, pl. 310.

This engaging composition shows a delightful corner of the book room at 7 Owens Row, Islington, London. A woman sits working at her folding writing desk which is perched on a draped tripod table by the window. Mr R.P. Cuff and his brother William rented rooms in this 18th-century house. The artist was an architect and illustration engraver, his brother a bookseller. Perhaps the young woman was the wife of one of them. The cluttered bookshelves may be evidence of William's stock, for there is an indication of commerce in the documents hanging on a wire hook.

John Ruskin commissioned illustrations to his second edition of *The Stones of Venice* from Richard Parminter, referring to him as 'the good Mr Cuff…'. Parminter exhibited designs for architecture at the Royal Academy from 1860 to 1876, but this drawing comes earlier in his career when aged 31, in 1855.

The particular charm of this watercolour is uncharacteristic for an architect, for it lovingly shows a true representation of a familiar, real room, as lived in during the mid 19th century.

Andrew Edmunds,
44 Lexington Street,
London W1R 3LH
Tel: 0171-437 8594
Fax: 0171-439 2551

A Trompe-l'oeil of assignats and
other Revolutionary ephemera
surrounding Callot's beggar.
Anonymous, French, circa 1796
or slightly later. Etching,
engraving, aquatint and roulette;
printed in black and red,
with watercolour.
Laid paper, watermark: 'F & D'
and dovecote.
58.5 x 49.5 cm (23 x 19 ½ in).

A memorial to the rise and fall of *assignats*, the Revolutionary paper money current from 1790 to 1796. During their short existence, 47 billion assignats were issued, supposedly guaranteed by the 'nationalised' *biens du Clergé*. Widespread forgery, massive inflation, and well-founded suspi-cion led to them falling to a tenth of their original face value. This was despite the introduction of the death penalty, not only for refusal to accept payment in *assignats*, but even for casting doubt on their credibility.

In the end, to restore public confidence, there was a symbolic *auto-da-fé* of most of the printing machinery in the Place Vendôme on 19 February 1796.

This print could have been made by an out-of-work *assignat* engraver or forger. His moral is represented by the central figure, copied from Jacques Callot's earlier print of a beggar.

Galerie Gismondi,
20 Rue Royale,
75008 Paris,
France
Tel: 33-1 42 60 73 89
Fax: 33-1 42 60 98 94

A Tulip, Peonies, Roses, Morning Glory and other flowers in a sculpted urn on a pedestal by Bartolomé Pérez (Madrid 1634-1698), circa 1666. Signed on the pedestal, 'Bme P'. Oil on glass.

34.2 x 28.6 cm (13 1/2 x 11 1/4 in). Provenance: The Comtesse Edouard de Saint Maurès (inscription on the backing board). Literature: W.B. Jordan and

P. Cherry, *Spanish Still Life from Velázquez to Goya*, National Gallery, London, 22 February - 21 May 1995, p. 198, note 10.

Richard Green,
44 & 39 Dover Street,
London W1X 4JQ
and
4 & 33 New Bond Street,
London W1Y 0SP
Tel: 0171-493 3939
Fax: 0171-629 2609

Landscape with birds and fruit by
Jacob Bogdani (Eperjes 1658 -

1724 London). Signed.
Oil on canvas.
101.6 x 127 cm (40 x 50 in).
Provenance: Private collection,
England.

Born in Eperjes, northern
Hungary, Bogdani came to
England in 1688 and was soon
taken up by the Court and aristocracy. He painted flowerpieces for

Queen Mary's 'Looking glasse
closett' at Hampton Court and
supplied paintings for King
William's palace at Dieren,
Holland. One of Bogdani's most
important patrons was Admiral
George Churchill, the Duke of
Marlborough's brother, whose
famous Windsor aviary provided
the inspiration for many of the
exotic birds that abound in

Bogdani's work. The birds in
this landscape are a chough
(*Pyrrhocorax pyrrhocorax*), a blue
and yellow macaw (*Ara ararauna*),
a scarlet macaw (*Ara macao*),
a sulphur-crested cockatoo
(*Cacatua galerita*), and a great tit
(*Parus major*).

Richard Green,
44 & 39 Dover Street,
London W1X 4JQ
and
4 & 33 New Bond Street,
London W1Y 0SP
Tel: 0171-493 3939
Fax: 0171-629 2609

Rustic figures on a road by James Stark (Norwich 1794 - 1859 London). Oil on canvas. 66 x 101.6 cm (26 x 40 in). Provenance: M.J. Newman, St James's, London. James Bostock, Hyde Lea, Stafford.

James Stark was a leading member of the Norwich School of painters, which included John Crome, John Sell Cotman and George Vincent. Stark studied with John Crome and, like him, was strongly influenced by the unassuming subject matter and naturalistic observation of 17th-century Dutch landscape painting. This peaceful scene of rustic travellers recalls the landscapes of Hobbema and Wynants. Stark excelled in painting the huge skies of East Anglia and the effects of light filtering through trees.

Richard Green,
44 & 39 Dover Street,
London W1X 4JQ
and
4 & 33 New Bond Street,
London W1Y 0SP
Tel: 0171-493 3939
Fax: 0171-629 2609

The return from the kermis by Pieter Brueghel the Younger (Brussels 1564/5 - 1637/8 Antwerp).
Signed 'P. BREUGHEL'.
Painted after 1616.
Panel 58 x 84.5 cm (22 ⁷/₈ x 33 ¹/₄ in).
Provenance: Two old collector's seals on reverse with initials 'EDD' and a crest with a goat's head. In an English private collection in the 19th century, then by descent. Literature: To be included in the forthcoming monograph and *catalogue raisonné*

of the work of Pieter Brueghel the Younger by Dr Klaus Ertz, no. 1301.

Pieter Brueghel is renowned for his crowded Flemish landscapes with peasant weddings and fairs, many of which are based on compositions by his father Pieter Brueghel the Elder (1520/25-1569). This painting, however, is an original composition by Pieter Brueghel the Younger. Teeming with incident, it combines the return from a kermis (fair) with the celebration of a return from

pilgrimage; on the left, a pilgrim with his badge is congratulated by a nobleman. The right of the picture shows St George's Fair with booths and merrymaking. The figure of St George as an archer appears on a banner above the inn, with the words '*Laet die boeren haer kermis houwen*' (Let the peasants have their fair) – possibly a protest against an edict of Emperor Charles V, which restricted fairs because of riotous behaviour.

Richard Green,
44 & 39 Dover Street,
London W1X 4JQ
and
4 & 33 New Bond Street,
London W1Y 0SP
Tel: 0171-493 3939
Fax: 0171-629 2609

Maternité: Madame Lebasque et ses enfants by Henri Lebasque (Champigné 1865 - 1937 Cannet). Signed. 1905.
Oil on canvas.
63 x 74 cm (24 ³/₄ x 29 in).
Provenance: Private collection.
Exhibited: Geneva, Musée du Petit Palais, 'L'enfance vue par les Grands Maîtres', 1979. Berlin, Staatliche Kunsthalle, 'Die gesellschaftliche Wirklichkeit der Kinder in der Bildenden Kunst', 1979-80, no. 328. Geneva, Musée du Petit Palais, 'Post-Impressionisme', 1980. Osaka, 'Trésors du Petit Palais à Génève', 1983, no. 30. Geneva, Musée de l'Athenée, 'Femmes et fleurs', 1988, illus. Marseilles, Forum des Arts, Palais de la Bourse, 'Trésors du Petit Palais de Génève', 1990, no. 67. Hiratsuka, 'Tarkoff et son temps', 1991, no. 57. Yamanashi, 'Paris, la joie de vivre', no. 83.
Literature: D. Speiss, *La peinture et l'enfant*, Paris, 1990, p. 19. Ed. Larousse, *L'Impressionisme et la peinture en plein air*, 1860 - 1914, Paris, 1992, p. 239.

Famed as a painter of 'joy' and 'light', Henri Lebasque's early work was influenced by the colour theories of Seurat and Signac. His exploration of *intimiste*, domestic subject matter was echoed in the work of younger artists such as Vuillard and Bonnard. Lebasque, with his friend Matisse, was a founding member of the Salon d'Automne in 1903. In 1905 the group of artists exhibiting there, among them Rouault, Derain, Vuillard, Manguin, and Matisse, were dubbed 'Les Fauves'. Lebasque adopted the Fauves' flatness of shape and colour, but blended it with a sophisticated, subtle fluidity.

The painting shows Lebasque's wife Catherine Fischer (known as Ella) and his daughter Marthe. Lebasque made many tender and delightful paintings of his family; a *Maternité* won a bronze medal at the Exposition Universelle in 1900.

Martyn Gregory,
34 Bury Street,
London SW1Y 6AU
Tel: 0171-839 3731
Fax: 0171-930 0812

Canton: the Western Factories by a
Chinese artist, circa 1835.
Oil on canvas.
48.2 x 72.4 cm (19 x 28 ¹/₂ in).

An unusual, angled view of the
'factories' or *hongs* of Canton
from the south-west, showing the
American, British and Dutch
flags. It was along this narrow
strip of land, fronting the Canton
River, that the Western trading
nations were allowed to establish
their bases. The painting dates
from between the early 1830s,
when the pagoda roof was
removed from Chung Qua's *hong*
(seen here to the left of the
American flagstaff), and the dev-
astating fire of 1841. Among the
many Chinese figures assembled
on 'Respondentia Walk' can be
seen street vendors, gamblers,
and itinerant barbers with their
characteristic pyramidal chests
and bamboo water-cylinders,

The Peabody Essex Museum
(Salem, Massachusetts), has a similar angled view of the factories
(M3793), but with a pair of goats
in the foreground and without the
horse and foal, (see Carl
Crossman, *The Decorative Arts of
the China Trade*, 1991, col. pl. 31).
Such angled compositions were
employed more typically by visiting Western artists, notably the
Daniells and George Chinnery;
the latter settled on the China
coast in 1825. For a view across
the same paddock looking south-
ward over the Canton River, see
Martyn Gregory Catalogue 59,
1992, no. 88.

Martyn Gregory,
34 Bury Street,
London SW1Y 6AU
Tel: 0171-839 3731
Fax: 0171-930 0812

Hong Kong and the harbour by a Chinese artist, circa 1870.
Oil on canvas.
34.2 x 51.4 cm (13 ½ x 20 ¼ in).

A view of the city of Victoria, Hong Kong Island, executed some 30 years after the establishment of the colony in 1841. Three conspicuous landmarks, all built some way back from the waterfront, are *(left to right)* St John's Cathedral, Government House (with its tall flagstaff), and the turreted Bishop's House; directly below Government House is the Clock Tower built in Pedder Street in 1865. On the summit of the Peak is the Signalling Station erected in 1861.

On the left in the crowded harbour is a three-decked covered 'receiving ship', used for the accommodation of sailors and naval administration; the vessel shown is perhaps HMS *Princess Charlotte*, which lay at anchor in Hong Kong harbour from 1858 to 1875. The smaller covered ship to the right flies the flag of the P&O Steamship Company, whose *hong* can be seen on the waterfront behind the American paddlesteamer.

Martyn Gregory,
34 Bury Street,
London SW1Y 6AU
Tel: 0171-839 3731
Fax: 0171-930 0812

Temple of Apollo Epicurius on Mt. Cotylus in Arcadia by Edward Dodwell (1767- 1832). Signed and dated verso 'Ed. Cam. O. orig. - Feb.1806', and inscribed as title. Pencil and watercolour. 25.4 x 45 cm (10 x 17 ³/₄ in).

The antiquary Edward Dodwell made his first visit to Greece with Sir William Gell in 1801. Returning to Italy, he was taken prisoner of war by the Buonaparte government, but was allowed to return to Greece on parole in 1805-6. Although the wealthy Dodwell took with him a hired draughtsman (Pomardi), he was himself an accomplished artist, and his surviving works form a valuable record of Greece before many of the spoliations of the 19th century. While sketching on the Acropolis, he himself witnessed the damage caused by the inept methods of Lord Elgin's employees.

Dodwell completed his tour despite many adventures, during which his camera obscura (to which the above inscription refers) was kicked to pieces by his donkey. He settled in Rome, where he married the daughter of Comte Giraud, and established his own museum of antiquities. After his death, this collection was sold to King Ludwig of Bavaria.

Iona Antiques,
P.O. Box 285,
London W8 6HZ
Tel: 0171-602 1193
Fax: 0171-371 2843

Eight children with a dog in the garden of a villa by an unknown English artist. Circa 1840. Canvas 71 x 91 cm (28 x 36 in). Provenance: The collection of K.J. Hewitt. Literature: *The English Scene*, a catalogue by The Rutland Gallery, June 1964, cover illustration.

This painting depicts a quintessentially English family group of children at the beginning of the Victorian era. To have so many children was not unusual in families of this period, but the family likeness shown here is remarkable.

The slight naivety of style gives this rare painting an added charm.

David Koetser Gallery,
Talstrasse 37,
8001 Zurich,
Switzerland
Tel: 41-1 211 52 40
Fax: 41-1 211 56 69

Red Gooseberries by Adrian Coorte (1685 - Middleburg - 1707). Signed and dated, 'A. Coorte 1705'. Oil on canvas. 31 x 23.5 cm (12 $\frac{1}{4}$ x 9 $\frac{1}{4}$ in). Provenance: E. Polak Collection, Rotterdam, 1940; J.S. Hirsh Collection, Bussum, 1954, and by descent through his family. Literature: Laurens J. Bol, *Adriaen Coorte*, p. 57-58, no. 65, illus. no. 33. Exhibited: 'Oude Kunst', Dordrecht Museum, 1953-4, cat. no. 26; 'Adriaen Coorte, Stilleven Schilder', Dordrecht, 1958, cat. no. 15, illus.; 'Zeeland in de beeldende Kunst der Lage Landen', Middleburg and Bruges, 1965, cat. no. 50, colour; 'The Age of Rembrandt', Tokyo/Kyoto, 1968-69, cat. no. 14; The Mauritshuis, The Hague, 1968; 'Masters of Middleburg', Amsterdam, 1984, cat. no. 56.

This beautiful little still life, which shows all the charm, simplicity and light of the master, is very rare in his *oeuvre*, being one of only three paintings of red gooseberries which are known.

Adriaen Coorte was first located in Zeeland, in Middleburg, and here in the archives of the old collections a record of these small still life paintings still exists. Coorte spe-cialised in painting still lifes with fruit and asparagus and, during a brief period (1696-98), shells. He seldom painted flowers. On a bare stone ledge, the 'Coorte ledge', the painter circumspectly and thoughtfully places one of his favourite subjects. Set against an unusual and extremely subtle background, the gooseberries stand out in a pure, clear light, 'Coorte's light'.

David Koetser Gallery,
Talstrasse 37,
8001 Zurich,
Switzerland
Tel: 41-1 211 52 40
Fax: 41-1 211 56 69

Skaters on a frozen river outside a town by Aert van der Neer (1603 - Amsterdam - 1677). Signed with the monogram, lower right. Oil on canvas. 45 x 55.3 cm (17 ³/₄ x 21 ³/₄ in). Provenance: Alfred de Rothschild (1842-1918), Seamore Place, London; Almina,

Countess of Caernarvon, 1918; Lord Rothermere, London, 1925; H. Harmsworth, 1st Viscount Rothermere, 1932; W.E. Duits, London, 1947; E. Fattorini Esq. Literature: P.G. Konody, *Works of Art in the Collection of Viscount Rothermere*, 1932, pl. 48; *Apollo*, vol. XXII, no. 132, December 1935, p. 331; *The Burlington Magazine*, May 1944; Dr Wolfgang Schulz, *Aert van der Neer, Catalogue Raisonné*, (forthcoming). Exhibited: Liverpool, City

School of Art, 'Exhibition of Dutch Masters', 1944, no. 11.

Aert van der Neer was born in Amsterdam in 1603, and almost nothing is known of his life. He excelled in moonlight views, usually of towns or of groups of fishermen's cottages on the bank of a river or canal, with boats and figures. He occasionally painted sunsets, but more often winter landcapes with figures amusing themselves on the ice, in which he was equalled only by Jacob van Ruisdael.

Aert van der Neer reinstated the monumental form of winter landscape first developed by Hendrick Averkamp half a century earlier, which he then customised in his own personal way. He utilised a variety of colouristic nuances, a diffusion and reflection of winter light, and a subtle definition of atmosphere thereto unseen in the history of winter landscapes. This painting is very rare, being one of van der Neer's 'blue' winter scenes.

**D.S. Lavender (Antiques) Ltd.,
26 Conduit Street,
London W1R 9TA
Tel: 0171-629 1782
Fax: 0171-629 3106**

Charles Dickens by William Moore of York, 1832. Watercolour on card. 20 x 25 cm (7 ⅞ x 9 ⅞ in). Provenance: Private collection, Alfriston, Devon (where Dickens' parents lived).

This is a rare watercolour of Charles Dickens, painted in 1832, when he was 21 years old.

William Moore (1790 - 1851), the portrait painter of York, was an expert artist working in oil, watercolour and pastel.

He was the father of Albert, Edwin, and Henry, all of whom became artists.

D.S. Lavender (Antiques) Ltd.,
26 Conduit Street,
London W1R 9TA
Tel: 0171-629 1782
Fax: 0171-629 3106

The death of Leonardo da Vinci in the arms of François I by Richard Cosway (1742 - 1821). Monochrome and grey wash, circa 1815.
23 x 30 cm (9 x 11 ⅞ in).

Provenance: Royal Cornwall Museum, Truro; Private collection. Exhibited: Scottish National Portrait Gallery, Edinburgh, and National Portrait Gallery, London,

'Richard and Maria Cosway, Regency Artists of Taste and Fashion', 1996.

Mallett Gallery,
141 New Bond Street,
London W1Y 0BS
Tel: 0171-499 7411
Fax: 0171-495 3179

The Artist's Studio – the painter sketching a model in historical costume by Louis Haghe (1806-1885). Signed and dated 1860. One of a pair. Watercolour over pencil, heightened with bodycolour.
67 x 91 cm (26 ¹/₂ x 36 in).

This watercolour, one of a pair, of impressive scale, depicts the artist's studio cluttered with furniture, tapestries, sculpture, and *objets d'art*. In Victorian England, studios were deliberately intended as showplaces reflecting the wide cultural taste of the artist, rather than as places of work.

Born in Belgium, Louis Haghe visited London in 1823, where he was granted the title of First Draughtsman to King William IV, and then later to Queen Victoria.

Mallett Gallery,
141 New Bond Street,
London W1Y 0BS
Tel: 0171-499 7411
Fax: 0171-495 3179

Three Pointers, the property of a Gentleman, in a landscape by the edge of a wood by Benjamin Killingbeck (fl. 1763-1783). Signed and dated 1777.

Oil on canvas.
107 x 152 cm (42 x 60 in).
Provenance: Collection of Michael Szell Esq., Chelsea, until 1987; Private collection, U.S.A.
Exhibited: London, The Free Society of Artists, 1779, as titled above, cat. no. 104.

Benjamin Killingbeck, a Yorkshireman, enjoyed early patronage of such distinguished patrons as the Marquis of Rockingham, the Earl of Eglinton, the Tattersalls and the Wentworth families, who were also major patrons of the developing genius of George Stubbs. Killingbeck's best known works are of a sporting nature, though he also produced landscapes and portraits.

Pointers first appeared in England around 1650, and Killingbeck's painting of this much depicted breed is interesting for the diversity of the dogs' poses, that leaves unresolved the question, at what are the pointers pointing? It is this sort of mild eccentricity that makes this, regrettably rare, artist so endearing to modern eyes.

Mallett Gallery,
141 New Bond Street,
London W1Y 0BS
Tel: 0171-499 7411
Fax: 0171-495 3179

Madame Leo d'Erlanger by Phillip
Alexius de Laszlo (1869-1937).
Oil on canvas.
87.5 x 114.5 cm (34 ¹/₂ x 45 in).

Born in Budapest, de Laszlo
gained recognition as a portrait
painter in Bavaria, Austria and
Germany, before visiting England
at the turn of the century. He
married into the Guinness family
and thus extended his clientele to
England as well as Ireland.

Like Sargent, he was attracted
to the elegance of 18th-century
English portraiture, in particular
that of Reynolds and
Gainsborough. With his own portraits, he aimed to show 'the spirit
by which the human form is
vitalised', and here we see
Madame Leo d'Erlanger in a
relaxed pose, 'no stiffness, no con-
straint – no posing' – words often
used to describe a de Laszlo portrait (*The British Portrait 1660-
1960*, Antique Collector's Club,
1991).

**Duncan R. Miller Fine Arts,
17 Flask Walk,
Hampstead,
London NW3 1HJ
Tel: 0171-435 5462
Fax: 0171-431 5352**

Circus Pony by John Maxwell,
RSA (1905 - 1962).
Signed and dated 1941. Oil on
board. 92 x 76 cm (36 x 30 in).
Provenance: Sir Michael
Redgrave. Exhibited: Royal
Scottish Academy, 1941, no. 33.
Arts Council of Great Britain,
'Paintings, Watercolours &
Drawings by W.G. Gillies &
John Maxwell', 1954, no. 35.
Arts Council of Great Britain,
'John Maxwell Memorial
Exhibition', 1963, no. 71,
catalogue, pl. 7.

The mysterious, evocative works
of John Maxwell are among
the most original and individual
to be found in 20th-century
Scottish Art.

John Maxwell studied under
Leger and Ozenfant. Although
he absorbed the teaching of
Cubism, it was to Symbolism
that he turned for inspiration, in
particular to the works of the
French artist, Odilon Redon, and
the lyrical, dream-like pictures
of the Russian-born artist,
Marc Chagall.

Maxwell's approach to his
work was intuitive and highly
inventive. With his great love of
music and poetry, he tended to
look inwards to the world of
dreams and imagination. A per-
fectionist by nature, he was
extremely self-critical and
destroyed so many of his own
pictures that only around 200
now remain.

Maxwell's oil paintings are
characterised by thickly applied
pigment which he often put on
with a palette knife to build up a
heavy impasto, working slowly
and often scraping out and
reworking certain areas, yet
always marrying the sensuous
charm of the medium to the very
essence of his vision. Moreover,
his use of rich, vivid colour draws
on the Scottish Colourist tradition. All these qualities are won-
derfully demonstrated in *Circus
Pony* which, as with most of his
oeuvre, transports the viewer to a
far continent at once familiar and
strange, enchanting and poignant.

**Duncan R. Miller Fine Arts,
17 Flask Walk,
Hampstead,
London NW3 1HJ
Tel: 0171-435 5462
Fax: 0171-431 5352**

Le Chapeau Jaune by John Duncan Fergusson (1874 - 1961). Signed verso. Circa 1909. Oil on canvas. 102 x 91 cm (40 x 36 in).
Provenance: Margaret Morris, the artist's wife.
Exhibited: Salon D'Automne, 1909. Japan British Exhibition, London 1910. Exposizione Internationale d'Arte, della Citta di Venezia 1912, no. 817. Sauchiehall Gallery, Glasgow, 'J.D. Fergusson Retrospective Exhibition', 1948, no. 15. Arts Council Scottish Tour, 'Fergusson Exhibition', 1954 - 1956, no. 15. Museum and Art Gallery, Glasgow, 'Exhibition of Scottish Painting', 1961, no. 151. Leicester Galleries, London, 'J.D. Fergusson', 1964, no. 4.

Although he was a truly cosmopolitan figure, Fergusson insisted at all times on the quintessentially Scottish qualities of his painting. As he himself put it, 'By painting I mean using oil paint as a medium to express the beauty of light on surfaces. What we used to call in Scotland "quality of paint" – with solidity and guts…'.

Having settled in Paris in 1907 and rented a studio in Montparnasse, Fergusson responded eagerly to the recent developments in painting, and soon evolved his own distinctive style. The sitter for this modish portrait was Elizabeth Dryden, who sat for Fergusson on several occasions. Elizabeth Dryden had been sent to Paris to cover theatre, ballet, opera, and race meetings for a magazine owned by Rodman Wanamaker of the Philadelphia department store. She was a friend of the artist Anne Estelle Rice, Fergusson's close companion.

Charles Marriott selected *Le Chapeau Jaune* as one of his 'Masterpieces of Modern Art' in 1922, in a collection which included paintings by Augustus John, Brangwyn, Lavery, Clausen, Monet, and Sickert. It was, he said, '…either the end of the old or the beginning of the new. It is more synthetic in treatment than anything else in the volume, but there is nothing in it which seems actually to contradict the experience of ordinary vision'.

Despite painting only in his spare time, John Quinton Pringle was a deeply committed artist who developed a fine and subtle style of painting which ranks alongside that of the Glasgow Boys and the Scottish Colourists.

Although Pringle was apprenticed to an optician as early as 1876, and ultimately became a highly skilled professional craftsman, he was inspired to take up art from an early age as he watched the many artists sketching at Langbank, where he had lived as a child. In 1883, he enrolled in evening art classes with the Glasgow School Board. Two years later, encouraged by the award of an Evening School Bursary, he attended morning and evening classes at Glasgow School of Art where he met, and became friends with, fellow student Charles Rennie Mackintosh. He continued these classes for ten years.

Pringle was intrigued by colour in art and particularly in miniatures. His interest in Impressionism also influenced his style, characterised by tiny fragments of pure colour alongside one another. He experimented increasingly and, from about 1900, his colour brightened and his brushstrokes became smaller and looser. With its fragmentary brushwork, possibly inspired by Le Sidaner, (who first exhibited at the Glasgow Institute in 1903), *Head of a Girl* ably conveys Pringle's masterly ability with colour and technique.

Duncan R. Miller Fine Arts,
17 Flask Walk,
Hampstead,
London NW3 1HJ
Tel: 0171-435 5462
Fax: 0171-431 5352

Head of a Girl by John Quinton Pringle (1864 - 1925). Signed and dated, '04. Oil on canvas. 41 x 31 cm (16 x 12 in). Provenance: The artist, and thence by family descent. Exhibited: Duncan R. Miller Fine Arts, 'Aspects of 20th Century Scottish Art', 1996, no. 6.

**Peter Nahum
At The Leicester Galleries,
5 Ryder Street,
London SW1Y 6PY
Tel: 0171-930 6059
Fax: 0171-930 4678**

Audience de Tribunal by Jean-Louis Forain RA (1852 - 1931). Signed and dated, 1908. Oil on canvas. 61 x 73.5 cm (24 x 29 in). Provenance: Dr Llobet, Buenos Aires; G. Salomon, Buenos Aires; Arthur Tooth & Sons Ltd, London 1964; R. Shand Kydd, 1964; Arthur Tooth & Sons Ltd, London; E. Cartwright, 1966; Peter Matthews, London; Lord Goodman, London to 1996. Literature: *The New York Times* (International Edition), 23 June 1964. Lilian Browse, *Forain, the Painter*, London, 1978, p. 51, 82-3, col. illus. p. 91, pl. VII.

Lilian Browse wrote, (op.cit.),
'This splendid courtroom scene is about the most colourful I know. Although the tone is low it is enlivened by the cherry dress of the woman leaning forward, the orange in her hat and the red of the plume and epaulettes of the standing guard. The concentration of the three main personages is beautifully caught. The tension is in the matter rather than in the execution, but this trait is general to Forain the painter – the difference between a *grand* and a *petit maître*.

'This artist, whose little *fin-de-siècle* paintings are those most prized on the market, really reached his height as a painter around the first decade of this century when, following in the footsteps of Daumier, he concentrated upon scenes in the Law Courts. The Goodman example *Audience de Tribunal* is undoubtedly one of the finest in this group – a painting that could hold its own in any company.'

**Peter Nahum At
The Leicester Galleries,
5 Ryder Street,
London SW1Y 6PY
Tel: 0171-930 6059
Fax: 0171-930 4678**

Kynance Cove by Frederic, Lord Leighton Bt PRA (1830 - 1896). Oil on panel.
12 x 20 cm (4 ½ x 7 ½ in).
Provenance: Christie's, London, '...The Collection of Ancient and Modern Pictures... of the late Lord Leighton', July 1896, lot 151, (£15 4s 6d), bought by Wickham Flower, his sale;

Christie's, London, '...the Collection of Wickham Flower Esq. deceased', December 1904, lot 32, sold to Claude Turner.
Literature: Ernest Rhys, *Frederic, Lord Leighton*, London, 1898, p. 93. Leonee & Richard Ormond, *Lord Leighton*, New Haven and London 1975, p. 120 & 176, cat. no. 475.
Exhibited: London, Royal Academy, 'Exhibition of Works by the late Lord Leighton of Stretton', 1897, no. 87 (lent by Wickham Flower).

For Leighton, drawings of nature

and oil sketches were private, in contrast to those public paintings from which he made his living. They served as aids to memory of places visited, often in escape from the pressures of his fame, and represented an entirely personal expression of his love for them; in fact, these landscapes were a form of relaxation away from the demands of his ever hungry public. It was for this reason that the majority of these treasured little panels were sold in his studio sale, as he had rarely thought to sell such intimate expressions during his lifetime.

Kynance Cove, a famous beach in south Cornwall, is close to Lizard Point and, with its dramatic beach formations, attracted artists throughout the Victorian period. Leighton is known to have painted other works in Cornwall, including *Near Kynance Cove* now in the collection at Leighton House, and also *Kynance Cove* exhibited at the Royal Academy exhibition, 'Frederic Leighton 1830 - 1896', in 1996 (private collection). Of the four pictures titled *Kynance Cove* listed in the 1896 Christie's catalogue, there is still one yet to be traced.

**Peter Nahum
At The Leicester Galleries,
5 Ryder Street,
London SW1Y 6PY
Tel: 0171-930 6059
Fax: 0171-930 4678**

Draft horses, Lumber Mill in the Forest of Dreux by Sir Alfred Munnings PRA (1878 - 1959). Signed. Oil on canvas. 50.8 x 61 cm (20 x 24 in). Provenance: James Connell & Sons, London. Literature: Sir Alfred Munnings KCVO, *An Artist's Life*, London 1950, p. 313-5.

As Official War Artist, Alfred Munnings wrote, (op.cit.),

'…two colonels, both in the Canadian Forestry Corps… persuading me that I must go with them and see the companies of Canadian Forestry who were then working in the many beautiful forests of France.' '…the area of the forest of Dreux, one of the finest in France, taking up fifteen square miles of ground.' '…Each company had a hundred and twenty horses, all half-bred Percheron types, mostly blacks and greys. A rivalry existed between the companies as to which had the best-conditioned teams. I painted pictures of these teams at work…'.

The Percheron, the strongest work horse in the world, originates from the Perche region in the South of Normandy. During the persecution of Protestants, and the famines of the 17th century, 70 per cent of the population of this region emigrated to Canada, along with large numbers from elsewhere in Normandy and Brittany. Strong ties between Quebec and individual villages are maintained to this day.

Galerie Neuse Kunsthandel,
Contrescarpe 14,
28203 Bremen,
Germany
Tel: 49-421 32 56 42
Fax: 49-421 32 86 11

Palamon and Arcite by William Hamilton (London 1750/1-1801). Signed and dated, 'W. Hamilton 1788'. Oil on canvas, 123.5 x 154 cm (48 ½ x 60 ½ in). Provenance: Csaky family; Anon sale, Dorotheum, Vienna, 25-27 April 1912, lot 325; Anon. sale,

Weizinger, Munich 29 May 1914, lot 50.

The subject of this scene would appear to be Palamon and Arcite, taken from Chaucer's *Canterbury Tales*, part II of the Knight's Tale. This tells how Theseus chanced upon Palamon and Arcite

duelling over their shared love for Emelyne, Ipolitas younger sister. In the present painting, the two women are shown pleading for the young men before Theseus, (shown in the centre), the husband of Ipolita.

**Newhouse Galleries, Inc.,
19 East 66th Street,
New York,
N.Y. 10021,
U.S.A.
Tel: 212-879 2700
Fax: 212-517 2680**

A Gentleman with his Daughter by Thomas de Keyser (circa 1596-1667). Trace of monogram and date at lower right on table leg, 'KT 16…'. Oil on copper. 50 x 42 cm (19 ¹/₂ x 16 ³/₈ in).

Thomas de Keyser was one of the most famous and successful portrait painters in Amsterdam until Rembrandt's arrival in 1632. When compared to Rembrandt and Hals, de Keyser's style is conservative and restrained, and his portraits record his sitters with accuracy and unpretentious frankness. He had a marvellous capacity for rendering the varied textures and aspects of objects in his paintings.

De Keyser was the son and pupil of Hendrick de Keyser, a sculptor. Although he was a painter, Thomas was also a stone merchant and a member of the stonemasons' guild in 1640. His painting activities appear to have diminished after this date.

De Keyser developed his own type of small, full-length portraits as well as the equestrian portraits that are among his most highly valued works. These paintings include some of the most esteemed and elegant portraits of the period, in which de Keyser used luminous blacks and subtle touches of colour to lend the works an extraordinary grace.

Here, as in the famous portrait of Constantijn Huygens (National Gallery, London), dated 1627, de Keyser used light to pick out details and focus attention, imbuing both works with an almost poetic refinement.

A closely comparable painting by de Keyser of the same man and his son (Norton Simon Museum, Pasadena, California) is dated 1631, suggesting a similar date for the present work.

**Newhouse Galleries, Inc.,
19 East 66th Street,
New York,
N.Y. 10021,
U.S.A.
Tel: 212-879 2700
Fax: 212-517 2680**

The Engagement between the Lion *and the* Elizabeth *off the Lizard, the Sloop* Du Thielly *in the distance taking the Young Pretender to Scotland, July 20th 1745* by Samuel Scott (1702-1772). Inscribed on the lining canvas, 'Action on the 9th of July 1745 between the Lion of 60 guns, Captain Percy Brett / and the Elizabeth of 64 guns, the doutelle in the distance making / her escape with the Pretender on board./ Painted for Admiral Lord Anson'. Oil on canvas. 102.7 x 152.3 cm (40 ½ x 60 in).

Provenance: Painted for Admiral Lord Anson (1682-1762); bought in 1931 for John, fourth Marquess of Bute (1881-1947) and thence by descent; full provenance available.

Literature: E. Waterhouse, *Painting in Britain 1530-1790*, London, 1953, p. 153; R. Kingzett, *A Catalogue of the Works of Samuel Scott*, Walpole Society, London, 1982, 31 (a), and p. 130-1, Appendix B.

Samuel Scott, an eminent painter of marines, was born in London in 1702 and began his career about 1725 by deliberately imitating the work of Willem van de Velde, painting sea battles and tranquil harbour views. He was soon well established in London, where he was a great friend of Hogarth. Scott also spent time in Italy, painting especially in Venice. He exhibited at the Royal Academy and in the Spring Garden Rooms, and retired to Bath after a long and prosperous career. He died there on 12 October 1772.

The engagement depicted in this painting took place on 20 July 1745, when the French man-of-war the *Elizabeth*, carrying arms to Scotland and escorting the Sloop *Du Theilly* with the Young Pretender on board, was sighted by Captain Percy Brett in the *Lion*, off the Lizard at four o'clock. Captain Brett made four drawings illustrating the successive stages of the encounter, and this picture is based on that of the final phase (in the Sandwich collection, Kingzett, op. cit. pl. 9a). The *Elizabeth* had seized the opportunity of a shift in the wind's direction to escape, and the *Lion*, much damaged and powerless to pursue, is seen firing a last raking volley.

Newhouse Galleries, Inc.,
19 East 66th Street,
New York,
N.Y. 10021,
U.S.A.
Tel: 212-879 2700
Fax: 212-517 2680

Dorothy Hodges (1752-1800), in a yellow dress, with pearls and a ribbon in her hair, in a feigned oval by Joseph Wright of Derby ARA (1734-1797). Oil on canvas. 76.6 x 64.1 cm (30 ¼ x 25 ¼ in). Provenance: by descent, through the sitter's eldest son, Thomas, to Rose Hodges; Humphrey Roberts by 1900; his sale, Christie's, 1908, lot 194, as by Sir T. Gainsborough RA, purchased by Agnews for Temple; John Howard Temple (d. 1922), Roberts's son-in-law, thence by descent.

Wright was known for his portraits, candle-light scenes, landscapes, and poetical and literary themes. He was born in 1734 in Derby and died there in 1797, being the first painter of note to prefer living outside London, and the first to explore the scientific interests of the industrial revolution. Several great industrialists of the day, including Wedgwood and Arkwright, were among his major patrons.

He was a pupil of Hudson in the 1750s. In the 1760s Wright experimented with the effects of candlelight on contemporary subjects, such as his famous *Experiment on a Bird in the Air-Pump*, now in the Tate Gallery. These new and daring works earned him tremendous acclaim.

From 1769 - 1771 he painted a series of portraits of members of prosperous middle class families in Liverpool. He then visited Rome and Naples, and witnessed Vesuvius erupting, another phenomenon of light which he incorporated into later works. Returning to England in 1775,

he settled in Bath before finally moving in 1777 to Derby.

The sitter in this painting was born Dorothy Cartwright in Marnham, Nottinghamshire in 1752. She married Thomas Hallett Hodges in 1775 and in the early years of their marriage lived at Serlby Hall,

Nottinghamshire. By 1784, they had moved to Hempstead Place, now Benenden School, in Kent. She died in 1800, and is buried, along with her husband who died the following year, in the family vault at Benenden Parish Church.

Noortman,
40-41 Old Bond Street,
London W1X 4HP
Tel: 0171-491 7284
Fax: 0171-493 1570
and
Vrijthof 49,
6211 LE Maastricht,
Holland
Tel: 31-43 321 6745
Fax: 31-43 321 3899

Nature morte by Maurice de Vlaminck (1876 - Paris - 1958). Signed. Canvas: 65.5 x 54 cm (25 ³/₄ x 21 ¹/₄ in). Provenance: Grosvenor Gallery, (Erick Estorick); acquired from above by Burt Lancaster. To be included in the forthcoming *catalogue raisonné* by the Wildenstein Institute.

Maurice de Vlaminck was, at various times, a professional racing cyclist, a double-bass player in a band, a soldier, a violin teacher, an anarchist, and a writer. His physical energy and love of speed, sound and movement expressed themselves in the vitality and vibrancy of his works. A fiercely independent figure, Vlaminck had no formal artistic training and believed that 'instinct is the foundation of art'. Van Gogh's choice and arrangement of colours, shown to full effect in the 1901 retrospective exhibition, had a profound influence on Vlaminck and his fellow Fauves and gave Vlaminck the confidence to express himself boldly in vivid colours. As his Fauve period came to an end, the 1907 Cézanne retrospective provided a major source of inspiration, encouraging him to further explore form and texture. Cézanne's influence was predominant until around 1910. The present painting probably dates from around 1914-1915, when Vlaminck was firmly embarked upon his most independent period of painting, confidently developing his own artistic personality, free from all other influences.

NOORTMAN

Noortman,
40-41 Old Bond Street,
London W1X 4HP
Tel: 0171-491 7284
Fax: 0171-493 1570
and
Vrijthof 49,
6211 LE Maastricht,
Holland
Tel: 31-43 321 6745
Fax: 31-43 321 3899

A calm, with a Dutch smalschip and an English man-o'-war at anchor by Willem van de Velde the Younger (Leiden 1633 - 1707 London). Circa 1655, signed with initials.
Panel: 50.8 x 45.5 cm (20 x 18 in).
Full details of provenance, exhibitions and literature available.

Although he continued to paint calms sporadically throughout the rest of his career, the younger Willem van de Velde specialised in the genre during the 1650s and early 1660s, refining his technique throughout these years. Most of these pictures are on a small scale, and they are of an extremely refined character, with carefully ordered compositions. The absence of any wind to disturb the sails or the surface of the water allows the objects in the picture, and their reflections, to be painted in sharp focus. This picture, which is beautifully preserved, is one of Willem van de Velde's finest early calms. Unlike many such pictures, it has no beach or jetty in the foreground, nor prominently at one side of the composition. The only plausible source of the ripples which break up the reflection of the vessel in the foreground (often provided in such works by a figure walking in the shallows) is the school of dolphins just breaking the surface.

Noortman,
40-41 Old Bond Street,
London W1X 4HP
Tel: 0171-491 7284
Fax: 0171-493 1570
and
Vrijthof 49,
6211 LE Maastricht,
Holland
Tel: 31-43 321 6745
Fax: 31-43 321 3899

Flowers in a glass vase by Ambrosius Bosschaert the Elder (Antwerp 1573 - 1621 The Hague). Signed with monogram and dated 1607. On copper: 38.5 x 26.5 cm (15 ⅛ x 10 ½ in). Provenance: Private collection, France.

Ambrosius Bosschaert the Elder played a pivotal role in introducing the botanical flower piece to the northern Netherlands in the first decades of the 17th century, and the genre was later developed further by his sons, Ambrosius, Johannes and Abraham, and his relatives, Balthasar and Johannes van der Ast.

This previously unpublished work, dated 1607, is one of the earliest known paintings by the artist. Two works dating from before 1607 are known, one dated 1605, from a private collection in Germany, and the second, dated 1606, which is conserved in the Museum of Art, Cleveland. Our painting compares very closely with the Cleveland picture. The same *roemer* glass is used as a vase in both pictures and the shape of the bouquet is also very similar. Many of the flower species typical of

Bosschaert's early period are present in our painting, for example, the red poppy anemone, the double white rose, and the yellow martagon lily. The tulips in the present painting are particularly well preserved, illustrating the artist's exquisitely fine technique of using many small parallel brushstrokes to express the curves of the petals.

**The O'Shea Gallery,
120A Mount Street,
London W1Y 5HB
Tel: 0171-629 1122
Fax: 0171-629 1116**

Le Perroquet cendre Tapire, a colour printed, copper plate engraving of a parrot after the illustration by Jacques Barraband. This magnificent bird featured in Francoise Levaillant's famous ornithological work, *Histoire Naturelle des Parroquets*, printed in Paris by Langlois, 1801 - 1805. Paper size: 33.5 x 24.5 cm (13 $\frac{1}{4}$ x 9 $\frac{3}{4}$ in).

Levaillant was a French explorer and natural historian who set out to compile what was to become the most beautiful and detailed work on parrots ever produced. To illustrate his writing he employed the talents of his friend and much acclaimed artist, the court painter Jacques Barraband. Between them they created the *Histoire*, which is universally recognised to this day as the most sumptuous and important study of parrots ever made. At a time when many new species of birds were being discovered and the New World was opening up, it is hardly surprising that these illustrations captured the public imagination to the extent that they did.

The plates themselves were partially printed in colour and the details finished by hand. No other artist has so successfully captured the fragility and finesse of the parrot's plumage. This is all the more surprising when they are placed in context, at a time when the widespread use of lithography was still in its infancy.

The French dominated the field of ornithological and animal art, and the Emperor Napoleon himself encouraged the work as part of his personal resolve to produce a series of lavish publications that would rival those undertaken by Louis XIV and promote the glories of Napoleonic France among the crowned heads and learned institutions of Europe.

Le Perroquet cendré Tapiré. Pl. 101.

Barraband pinx.ᵗ   De l'Imprimerie de Langlois.

**The O'Shea Gallery,
120A Mount Street,
London W1Y 5HB
Tel: 0171-629 1122
Fax: 0171-629 1116**

The Craven Heifer, an etching and colour printed stipple engraving by J. Whessell after the painting by Fryer. Published in January 1812 by the Revd. William Carr of Bolton who also bred and fed the animal. Framed size 67.5 x 77.5 cm (26 ¹/₂ x 30 ¹/₂ in).

The heifer stands facing left against a rural landscape with a Gothic ruin. The original Craven heifers were longhorns, but the repeated use of shorthorn bulls eventually resulted in a shorthorn type. This particular cow was bred in 1807 by the Revd. Carr on the Duke of Devonshire's estate. She weighed 176 stone and four pounds, and was so large that a special door, twice the normal width, had to be built to enable her to enter her loose-box. In the early 19th century,

there was a fashion for breeding the largest domestic animals possible, and it became a matter of pride with the owners of cattle such as the *Craven Heifer* to have their prize animals recorded.

The artists recruited by breeders were required, above all, to create a flattering portrait and exaggeration was totally acceptable. The breeders, in turn, used subsequent printed reproductions to advertise their prowess as creators of prize animals. Not everyone approved of this fatten-

ing of beasts, almost to a level of caricature. The painter, Thomas Bewick, lamented,

'Many of the animals were, during this rage for fat cattle, fed up to as great a weight and bulk as it was possible for feeding to make them; but this was not enough; they were to be figured monstrously fat before the owners of them could be pleased. Painters were found who were quite subservient to this guidance, and nothing else could satisfy.'

Richard Philp,
59 Ledbury Road,
London W11 2AA
Tel: 0171-727 7915
Fax: 0171-792 9073

Anne of Austria by Ferdinand Elle (1612 - 1689). Oil on canvas. 112 x 84 cm (44 x 33 in).

Louis Elle the elder, known as Ferdinand, was born in Paris, the son of a Flemish artist. In 1657 he became professor at the Academy, though in 1681 he was excluded for being a Protestant. He was much admired as a portrait painter, exhibiting at the Salon in 1673. His portraiture was influenced by Van Dyck, and examples of his work can be found in a number of museum collections including Bordeaux, Reims, and the Louvre.

This three-quarter length portrait of the wife of Louis XIII relates to the portrait of the same sitter in the Chiswick House collection. Both paintings have a similar composition, but in our example the Queen is shown standing before a drape, which is drawn back to reveal an early 17th-century long gallery.

Anne of Austria (1601 - 1666) was the daughter of Philip III of Spain. She married Louis XIII in 1615 and, on his death in 1643, became Regent of France for her son, Louis XIV (1638 - 1715).

Richard Philp,
59 Ledbury Road,
London W11 2AA
Tel: 0171-727 7915
Fax: 0171-792 9073

Head of a Young Boy. Florentine, circa 1585. Circle of Alessandro Allori (1535-1607). Inscribed, 'n.288' and '209'.
Black and white chalk on blue paper, shaped.
15.7 x 11.3 cm (6 ¹/₈ x 4 ¹/₂ in).
In a fine English 17th-century carved oak frame.

This drawing, with its emphasis on line, is characteristic of Florentine mannerist painters in the late seicento. Allori was the most distinguished artist in the circle of refined masters whose influence is evident in this study.

Pyms Gallery,
9 Mount Street,
Mayfair,
London W1Y 5AD
Tel: 0171-629 2020
Fax: 0171-629 2060

Study for A Hopeless Dawn by
Frank Bramley RA (1857-1915),
inscribed with title on stretcher.
Oil on canvas.
32.7 x 44 cm (12 ³/₄ x 17 ¹/₄ in).

Provenance: Mlle. Caisson,
91 Rue George Clémenceau,
Cannes.

In 1888, what was to become
Frank Bramley's most celebrated
work, *A Hopeless Dawn* (Tate
Gallery, London) was purchased
by the Chantrey Bequest for the
national collection. It was painted
in a tiny cottage at Newlyn and
records the night vigil of two
women who wait for a fisherman

who will not return. It was, in
the words of a proponent of
the Newlyn School, a perfect
blend '...of human drama and of
beautifully executed and carefully
observed effects of light and of
colour and tone'. This *première
idée* for *A Hopeless Dawn* well
illustrates the process of realiza-
tion in Bramley's work, using
broad, square-shaped strokes,
painting across the forms in the
characteristic Newlyn manner.

The picture differs from the finished work only in points of
detail. An open Bible on the
woman's knee and a loaf of bread
on the table are the principal
additions in the finished work,
reinforcing the guttering candles
and well-observed morning light
of the present sketch.

Pyms Gallery,
9 Mount Street,
Mayfair,
London W1Y 5AD
Tel: 0171-629 2020
Fax: 0171-629 2060

Study for Earl Morley addressing the House of Lords (The Ratification of the Irish Treaty) by Sir John Lavery RA, RSA, RHA, (1856-1941). Signed lower right and extensively inscribed.

Oil on canvas-board.
25 x 35 cm (9 ⁷/₈ x 13 ³/₄ in).

Throughout his career, Lavery saw himself as an artist-reporter. In 1921, for instance, when negotiations for the Irish Treaty were taking place, he produced portraits of all the members of the Irish delegation. As the bill passed from the Commons to the Lords in December of that year, he painted a record of the event

in two commemorative canvases. The practice of making small head studies for large works began in 1888 when Lavery was working on *The State Visit of Queen Victoria to the International Exhibition, Glasgow*. In the present case, *Earl Morley addressing the House of Lords* (Glasgow Art Gallery and Museums) was painted from a compositional study (National Gallery of Ireland) and from the detailed notes of the

protagonists contained in the present sketch, the majority of whom are identified. An ironic addition to this miscellany is the head of Hazel Lavery, seen at right angles to the others, in the head dress of Pavlova in *La Morte du Cygne* 1913 (Tate Gallery). The ghost of Lady Lavery thus symbolically presides over the scene, as she did over the dinner tables at which the negotiations were conducted.

Pyms Gallery,
9 Mount Street,
Mayfair,
London W1Y 5AD
Tel: 0171-629 2020
Fax: 0171-629 2060

A Camp of a thousand Men formed by Augustus Cleveland three miles from Bhagalpur, with his mansion in the distance by William Hodges RA (1744-1797). Inscribed as title by the artist on a label, verso. Oil on canvas. 122 x 160 cm (48 x 63 in). Provenance: Sir George Christie, Bt, DL.

In 1782, the artist-explorer William Hodges, who had travelled with Captain Cook, made a second visit to India, where he had previously been introduced to Augustus Cleveland, the magistrate of Bhagalpur. Cleveland had just formed a regiment of sepoys, recruited from the Paharia tribesmen, which was to be in the employment of the East India Company. These are seen at their newly established camp in the present work. In the brilliant reds of the uniforms and the arrangement of figures parallel to the plane of the picture, Hodges' view of Cleveland's camp anticipates splendid military group portraits like Wheatley's *Volunteers* in the National Gallery of Ireland and Stubbs' *Soldiers of the Tenth Light Dragoons* in the collection of Her Majesty The Queen.

**Pyms Gallery,
9 Mount Street,
Mayfair,
London W1Y 5AD
Tel: 0171-629 2020
Fax: 0171-629 2060**

Le Drap Vert by Roderic O'Conor (1860-1940). Signed top left, 'O'Conor '13'. Inscribed verso in orange chalk 'Le drap vert, Roderic O'Conor'. Oil on panel.
46 x 37.5 cm (18 ⅛ x 14 ¾ in).
Provenance: Studio of the artist, sold Hôtel Drouot, Paris, 7 February 1956; Sotheby's, London, 1 May 1957, lot 131, bought Widdup; Redfern Gallery, London, sold to H.E. Bates, May 1964; Keyser Gallery, 1980.

After his last trip to Brittany in 1904, O'Conor remained in Paris for the following eight years. A brief reconnaissance trip to the Bay of Cassis is recorded late in 1912 and this experience had an immediate effect upon his work. Almost in anticipation of the glowing hues which he would encounter on his second, longer, visit in the summer of 1913, O'Conor's studio-pieces took on an intensity of colour and a weight of impasto which conveys the full richness of his mature work. Residual notes of complementary colour, reflections of green in the flesh tints and the dappled green and mauve backdrop serve to remind us that this is the work of one of the original

Post-Impressionists who, through the experience of Fauvism and Intimisme, had forged a personal style. Comparisons between *Le Drap Vert* and the early Fauve nudes of Matisse and Marquet are apposite.

**Spink & Son Ltd.,
5 King Street,
St James's,
London SW1Y 6QS
Tel: 0171-930 7888
Fax: 0171-839 4853**

Henrietta Cozens by Johann Friederich August Tischbein (1750 - 1812). Signed and dated 1787. Oil on canvas. 62 x 51 cm (24 ½ x 20 in). Provenance: James Harris, 1st Earl of Malmesbury, commissioned from the artist as a gift to the sitter, Henrietta Cozens (1767 - 1829), and by family descent to 1996.

Henrietta Cozens, with her sister Jane, were closely connected for a number of years with the household of James Harris, 1st Earl of Malmesbury. From surviving correspondence, Jane appears to have been a governess to the Harris children and Henrietta may have occupied a similar position. The high regard in which Henrietta was held is evident from the annuity which Lord Malmesbury settled on her and her sister, as well as his commissioning of this portrait from Tischbein, who also painted the Malmesbury children at about the same time. Henrietta was a niece of the artist Alexander Cozens, and became the wife of the Revd. T. B. Percival.

Tischbein was born in Maastricht and studied painting under his uncle, a well-known history painter. He finished his education in France and Italy under the patronage of the Prince of Waldeck who

appointed Tischbein the Court Painter. He subsequently practised as a portrait painter at the Hague, where the present portrait was executed, as well as in Dessau and Leipzig, where he became Director of the Academy of Painting. Tischbein enjoyed an elevated patronage as a portrait painter with many of the Royal families of Germany sitting to him, as well as such luminaries as Schiller, Lavater and Mesmer.

SPINK & SON LTD

Spink & Son Ltd.,
5 King Street,
St James's,
London SW1Y 6QS
Tel: 0171-930 7888
Fax: 0171-839 4853

Summer Landscape by Paul Nash (1889-1946). Pen and black ink and watercolour. 52 x 39.4 cm (20 ½ x 15 ½ in).

In July 1914, Paul Nash and his fiancée Margaret Odeh went to stay with the poet, Gordon Bottomley, and his wife, Emily, at their home, The Shieling, at Silverdale, near Carnforth in Lancashire. Nash was unacquainted with the north of England and the new landscape of hills and lakes excited and stimulated him. During this holiday, Nash started 26 drawings, of which this is one. Others include *The Monkey Tree*, (now in the Victoria and Albert Museum), the subject of which was in Bottomley's garden, and *The Apple Pickers* which is now in the Cecil Higgins Museum in Bedford.

**Alistair Sampson Antiques Ltd.,
120 Mount Street,
London W1Y 5HB
Tel: 0171-409 1799
Fax: 0171-409 7717**

Two King Charles spaniels, one a puppy attributed to a member of the Clarke family. Mid 19th century. Oil on canvas. 67.3 x 86.4 cm (26 ½ x 34 in).

Members of the Clarke family are best known for their charming studies of dogs – particularly those showing King Charles and Cavalier King Charles spaniels.

**Stoppenbach & Delestre Ltd.,
25 Cork Street,
London W1X 1HB
Tel: 0171-734 3534
Fax: 0171-494 3578**
and by appointment at
**36, Rue Laffitte,
75009 Paris, France
Tel: 33-1 48 24 05 01
Fax: 33-1 48 24 06 12**

Jean Flameng, neveu de l'artiste by François Flameng (1856 - 1923). Signed and dated, upper right, 'François Flameng 1900'. Oil on canvas. 146 x 92.5 cm (57 $^1/_2$ x 36 $^1/_2$ in). Provenance: Private collection, France.

François Flameng was a well-known society portrait artist whose works include the 1908 portrait of Queen Alexandra which hangs in Buckingham Palace. He exhibited in London and Paris, his style of painting being considered highly fashionable. This portrait is of his nephew, Jean Flameng.

**Stoppenbach & Delestre Ltd.,
25 Cork Street,
London W1X 1HB
Tel: 0171-734 3534
Fax: 0171-494 3578**
and by appointment at
**36, Rue Laffitte,
75009 Paris, France
Tel: 33-1 48 24 05 01
Fax: 33-1 48 24 06 12**

The Inauguration of the Great Exhibition; the Crystal Palace by Eugene Lami (1800 -1890). Signed and dated, lower right, 'E. Lami 1851'. Watercolour and gouache.
53.4 x 39.4 cm (21 x 15 ½ in).
Provenance: Prince Anatole Demidoff, San Donato, Florence; auction: 'Collections de San Donato: Quatrième Vente', Messrs. Pillet & Petit, Paris, March 1870, no. 327.

Eugene Lami was commissioned to paint a series of eight watercolours of the Great Exhibition of 1851 for his most loyal and generous patron, Prince Demidoff. The present painting was one of two external views, the suite also comprising scenes of the Russian, English, French, Indian, Prussian, and Austrian sections. Prince Demidoff wrote to praise his friend the artist, 'You have given to all your gentlemen and ladies a special quality which is the essence of the civilisation of 1852, which will remain a key moment within your compositions...'. The series was executed between August 1851 and February 1852.

The work portrays the main entrance of the Crystal Palace at the central intersection of the nave and transepts, where an enormous glass fountain was one of the first sights upon entering the building. The artist delights in the variety of fashions and postures of the visitors in the foreground – a visiting provincial family and an officer with an elegant lady. The line of carriages waiting to deliver their visitors disappears into the distance. Such a characterisation of a scene caused Baudelaire to describe Lami as 'a poet of dandyism, almost English in the love for things aristocratic'.

Stoppenbach & Delestre Ltd.,
25 Cork Street,
London W1X 1HB
Tel: 0171-734 3534
Fax: 0171-494 3578
and by appointment at
36, Rue Laffitte,
75009 Paris, France
Tel: 33-1 48 24 05 01
Fax: 33-1 48 24 06 12

Le Parc du Trocadero by Stanislas Victor Edouard Lépine (1835 - 1892). Circa 1879. Signed, lower left, 'S. Lepine'. Oil on panel. 24.6 x 16.4 cm (9 ³/₄ x 6 ¹/₂ in). Provenance: collection Goerg, Paris; collection Hazard, Paris; collection Sayag, Paris; private collection.
Exhibited: Galeries Durand-Ruel, Paris, 1892, 'Stanislas Lépine', no. 29. Literature: Robert and Manuel Schmit, *Stanislas Lépine; catalogue raisonné de l'oeuvre peint*, Paris, 1993, no.182, illus. p.74.

Though largely self-taught, Lépine studied with Corot in 1866 and was influenced by Jongkind. He painted portraits and marine themes, though river scenes and Paris views were his prime subjects. Lépine exhibited with the Impressionists in their first exhibition in 1874, but his style had a greater affinity with the art of the pre-Impressionists such as Corot and Daubigny. Lépine's first Salon entry was in 1853, but he did not gain official recognition until 1884, when he received an honorable mention. He went on to win a first class medal at the Exposition Universelle of 1889. His work has been reappraised in recent years and deservedly so, as he was a painter of great charm and quality.

The Parc du Trocadero was on the site of the Trocadero in Paris over-looking the Eiffel Tower. The Parc was redeveloped in the 1930s and the imposing Palais du Trocadero, with its twin minarets, was demolished. The Parc was one of the great venues for social gathering and recreation in Paris. The Palais contained, among other things, the Ethnological Museum where Picasso, Derain and others used to study the art of Africa and Oceanea in the first decade of this century.

Rafael Valls Ltd.,
11 Duke Street,
St James's,
London SW1Y 6BN
Tel: 0171-930 1144
Fax: 0171-976 1596

A Gentleman, possibly William Eden, first Lord Auckland, MP, (1744-1814), a head study, unfinished, by Sir Thomas Lawrence (1769-1830).
Oil on canvas.
76.2 x 63.5 cm (30 x 25 in).
Provenance: possibly Sir Edmund Davies.
Literature: K. Garlick, *A Catalogue of the Paintings, Drawings and Pastels of Sir Thomas Lawrence*, London,1964, p. 208, no. 3;
K. Garlick, *Sir Thomas Lawrence*, Oxford, 1989, no. 863.

Garlick (op.cit.) dates this picture to the early 1790s. He also notes that the portrait bears 'a certain but not convincing' likeness to Lawrence's *Portrait of William Eden, 1st Baron Auckland* (Garlick op. cit. no. 53), which was commissioned for Christchurch, Oxford, and for which a sitting is recorded in 1792.

Sir Thomas Lawrence was the foremost British portrait painter of his age and his paintings epitomised the Regency style. As an infant prodigy, he drew remarkable pencil likenesses at the age of ten. He came to London in 1787, and attended the Royal Academy in 1788. His full length portrait of Queen Charlotte, exhibited in 1790, established his reputation as the finest portrait painter in the new

romantic style.

Lawrence succeeded Reynolds as Painter in Ordinary to the King in 1792. At this time he painted several historical and religious pictures, such as *Satan Summoning his Legions*, but the demand for his society portraits left him little time to pursue this theme.

His reputation was further enhanced when he was commissioned by the Prince Regent to paint all the principal characters in the downfall of Napoleon, which became the great series of portraits in the Waterloo Chamber at Windsor.

Until his death in 1830, Lawrence exhibited at the Royal Academy, becoming its President in 1820.

Rafael Valls Ltd.,
11 Duke Street,
St James's,
London SW1Y 6BN
Tel: 0171-930 1144
Fax: 0171-976 1596

A Trompe-l'oeil of letters, pamphlets, a quill, sealing waxes, a miniature of Charles I, and other objects by Evert Collier (active 1680-1706), Dutch School. Signed. Oil on Canvas. 48.5 x 83.5 cm (19 x 32 ³/₄ in).

Evert Collier was a Dutch still life painter in the style of Jan Vermeulen or Pieter Potter. His main subjects were *Vanitas* with musical instruments and books, a globe and a nautilus shell, piled together on the corner of a table, on a velvet cloth with gold fringes. He was especially fond of painting open books, sheets of paper with writing or drawing on them, rich jewellery, and pearl necklaces. His portraits are rare.

Museums where examples of Collier's work can be found include The Hague, London (Tate Gallery), and Vienna.

Johnny Van Haeften Ltd.,
13 Duke Street,
St James's,
London SW1Y 6DB
Tel: 0171-930 3062
Fax: 0171-839 6303

An Italianate landscape with herders and their flocks halted on a path by Nicolaes Berchem (Haarlem 1620 - 1683 Amsterdam). Signed. Oil on panel. 36 x 45 cm (14 x 17 ³/₄ in).

Nicolaes Berchem was a highly versatile painter who was equally at home painting landscapes, architecture, figures, and animals. He worked in Italy between 1642 and 1645, and this picture is typical of his middle period in which Italianate subjects became dominant, and in which the whole

scene is bathed in the golden light of a southern sunset.

A related, signed pen-and-wash drawing of this composition was sold at Sotheby's, Amsterdam, 25 April 1983, lot 60.

Johnny Van Haeften Ltd.,
13 Duke Street,
St James's,
London SW1Y 6DB
Tel: 0171-930 3062
Fax: 0171-839 6303

A still life of fruit in a porcelain bowl by Osias Beert, the Elder (circa 1570 - Antwerp - 1624). On panel: 53.3 x 74.5 cm (21 x 29 ¼ in). Provenance: Private European collection.

Osias Beert the Elder was a Flemish painter of breakfast still lifes and flowers. Little is known about his life. He was born around 1570 in Antwerp where he became an apprentice of the Guild in 1596, and the Master in 1602. He married the daughter of the painter Ykens. Beert painted vessels of metal, glass and earthenware arranged, apparently at random, on a table-top with a dark background. He often painted porcelain and pewter plates or bowls laden with apples, peaches, strawberries, hazelnuts, chestnuts or oysters. He also painted exuberant bunches of flowers displayed in glass or earthenware vases or flat porcelain bowls. Our painting is an unpublished, recent discovery from a private European collection.

Johnny Van Haeften Ltd.,
13 Duke Street,
St James's,
London SW1Y 6DB
Tel: 0171-930 3062
Fax: 0171-839 6303

Peaches, grapes, a gourd, cherries, a corn cob, ears of corn with butterflies, a snail, a caterpillar and a mouse by a mossy tree stump by Abraham Mignon (Frankfurt 1640 - 1679 Utrecht).
Signed 'A. Mignon:fe'.
Oil on canvas.
61 x 51 cm (24 x 20 in).
Provenance: Anon. Sale, Dorotheum, Vienna, 10 October 1943, lot 110, Linz Museum, Austria, collecting point 1939-1945. Literature:
M. Kraemer-Noble, *Abraham Mignon*, Leigh-on-Sea, 1973, p. 71, no. B267.

Abraham Mignon was among the most gifted of Jan Davidsz. de Heem's pupils. He had a great fondness for showing light reflected from a variety of different surfaces – stone, fruit, leaves and petals. This particular forest floor, seen at night, owes its style to the work of Otto Marsens van Schrieck and is probably an early work by Mignon. It shows his excellent draughtsmanship and his ability to imbue even the simplest subject with a sense of drama.

**William Weston Gallery,
7 Royal Arcade,
Albemarle Street,
London W1X 4JN
Tel: 0171-493 0722
Fax: 0171-491 9240**

Le Visage Encadré - Etude de Mme Helleu by Paul Helleu (1859 - 1927). Circa 1898.
Drypoint in colours.
27.8 x 39.8 cm (10 ⁷/₈ x 15 ⁵/₈ in).
Literature: Montesquiou, *Paul Helleu Les Pointes Sèches*, 1913.

Le Visage Encadré is one of the most famous colour drypoints in Helleu's *oeuvre*, and one of his most beautiful portraits of his wife. Helleu was the greatest French draughtsman of the era of the *belle époque*. He understood to perfection the special nature of

drypoint line – how it combines linear definition and surface texture within a single stroke. The flow and style of his drawing epitomises the atmosphere of refined elegance which characterised French art and society around the turn of the century.

Christopher Wood,
20 Georgian House,
10 Bury Street,
London SW1Y 6AA
Tel. and Fax: 0171-839 3963

Calm Waters, Scarborough,
Yorkshire by Atkinson Grimshaw
(1836-1893).
Signed and dated 1880.
Oil on canvas.
81.3 x 119.4 cm (32 x 47 in).

Atkinson Grimshaw is now famous for his night scenes, particularly of docks and city streets. This unusually large picture is a view of the harbour at Scarborough in Yorkshire, where Grimshaw had a house, a remarkable Gothic folly which he

referred to as his castle by the sea. His main house was Knostrop Hall, near Leeds, which he also often painted. Grimshaw rarely exhibited his work in public, as he worked almost exclusively for private patrons in the north.

Christopher Wood,
20 Georgian House,
10 Bury Street,
London SW1Y 6AA
Tel. and Fax: 0171-839 3963

Portrait study of an Italian Girl by Valentine Cameron Prinsep RA (1838-1904). Signed and dated '84. Inscribed, 'a mon ami Albanesi, '97'. Oil on canvas. 61 x 51 cm (24 x 20 in).

Val Prinsep was a well-known late Victorian painter of portraits and historical subjects. As a young man, he assisted the Pre-Raphaelites with the decorations of the Oxford Union. Later he came under the influence of both Leighton and Watts. He married the daughter of the great collector F.R. Leyland, and became a noted society portrait painter. He was elected an RA in 1894.

In 1899, he exhibited a portrait of a Signor Carlo Albanesi, to whom this portrait study is dedicated. Perhaps it is a portrait of Albanesi's wife or daughter. In the photograph of Prinsep in his studio *(right)*, it can clearly be seen on the easel in front of him.

**Christopher Wood,
20 Georgian House,
10 Bury Street,
London SW1Y 6AA
Tel. and Fax: 0171-839 3963**

The Calling Card by William Fitz
(working 1880-1891).
Signed and dated. Oil on canvas.
54 x 40.6 cm (21¼ x 16 in).

Little is known of the career of
William Fitz, who exhibited two
pictures at the Royal Academy,
both interiors. This charming
scene clearly depicts the entrance
hall of a London house. The butler is scrutinising a calling card
left by a visitor. The pictures on
the wall and the large classical
sculpture on the left suggest that
the owner of the house may be a
collector.

Christopher Wood,
20 Georgian House,
10 Bury Street,
London SW1Y 6AA
Tel. and Fax: 0171-839 3963

Early Spring by William J. Webbe (working 1853-1878). Signed with monogram and dated 1856. Oil on board. 20.5 x 58.4 cm (18 x 23 in).

William J. Webbe was one of a small group of Pre-Raphaelite artists working in the circle of William Holman Hunt. Like Hunt, he specialised in small, intensely Ruskinian close-ups of plants, rocks and birds, also frequently depicting sheep. These paintings reflect the Ruskinian philosophy that the artist should record nature as it is, 'rejecting nothing, selecting nothing'. Webbe visited the Middle East, as Hunt did, and painted scenes of Arab life around Jerusalem. He exhibited at the Royal Academy from 1853 to 1878.

Silver, Jewellery and Objets de Vertu

(including Sheffield Plate, Bijouterie, Fabergé, Snuff-Boxes, Miniatures, Enamels and Russian Works of Art)

A silver-gilt tankard with medals of Pallas Athene, Venus and Diana after Virgil Solis, Cornelius or Elias Gross, Augsburg, circa 1560.
Galerie Neuse Kunsthandel

A black natural pearl, diamond, and emerald sautoir by David Webb.
S.J. Phillips Ltd

...ail of Etoile, a fine gold, ...ue à jour and diamond ...dant by Antoine Bricteux, ...ed, circa 1908.
...ema Gallery

A late 18th-century tortoiseshell étui with silver piqué decoration, fitted with its original silver accoutrements, English, circa 1790.
Halcyon Days

A La Vieille Russie, Inc.,
781 Fifth Avenue,
New York,
N.Y. 10022
U.S.A.
Tel: 212-752 1727

Top, A foiled pink topaz necklace and a pair of earrings mounted in gold, English, circa 1800.
Left to right, an amethyst and diamond brooch mounted in platinum and gold, French, circa 1910; two gold, nephrite jade, and enamel buttons by Fabergé, in the style of 17th-century silver buttons, each wearable as a pendant; a pair of cabochon sapphire and diamond 'geese' brooches mounted in platinum, American, circa 1940.

**A La Vieille Russie, Inc.,
781 Fifth Avenue,
New York,
N.Y. 10022
U.S.A.
Tel: 212-752 1727**

A selection of Russian *objets* including (*clockwise from upper left*) a brown porcelain egg, period of Nicholas II (1896-1917), height 11.4 cm (4 ¼ in); a lavender porcelain egg, period of Nicholas II; a painted crucifix in enamel mount with silver trim, 18th century, inscribed, 'The Cross is the Protector of the Universe; The Cross is the Beauty of the Church; The Cross is the Power of the Tzar; The Cross is the Testimony of Faith; The Cross is the Voice of Glory.'; a large gilt porcelain egg with Madonna and Child, period of Nicholas I (1825-1855); a diptych icon of the crucifixion and Sts Michael, Stephan, and John the Warrior, in a brass frame with silver covers, maker P.N., circa 18th century; a gilded silver-mounted carved boxwood triptych icon, 16th century (*top*: prophets and kings, *middle*: Deisis, *bottom*: saints); a cast brass icon of St George, 15th-16th century; an icon of Christ the Pantocrator in a shaded enamel frame with seed pearl robe, maker C.E., Moscow, circa 1890.

A La Vieille Russie, Inc.,
781 Fifth Avenue,
New York,
N.Y. 10022
U.S.A.
Tel: 212-752 1727

A selection of gold snuff-boxes
and other small boxes, variously
decorated with enamel,
diamonds, mother-of-pearl or
lacquer, dating between circa
1745 and circa 1809.

A La Vieille Russie, Inc.,
781 Fifth Avenue,
New York,
N.Y. 10022
U.S.A.
Tel: 212-752 1727

Above, a diamond and blue
enamel bangle, convertible to a
brooch, in a fitted case.
Hunt & Roskell, English,
circa 1840. Diameter of brooch
3.2 cm (1 ¼ in).
Above right, a lapis lazuli clock
with gold wreath bezel and
mounts, and white enamel dial.
Fabergé, workmaster
Henrik Wigstrom.
Right, two circular gold and
brilliant translucent enamel
frames set with diamonds.

Fabergé, workmaster Michael
Perchin; the frames consecutively
numbered 54610 and 54611.
Height 6.6 cm (2 ⁵/₈ in)
Diameter 7.4 cm (2 ¹⁵/₁₆ in).

Asprey,
165-169 New Bond Street,
London W1Y 0AR
Tel: 0171-493 6767
Fax: 0171-491 0384

A fine George III hot water urn
by Francis Butty and Nicholas
Dumee, London, 1770.
Height 59.7 cm (23 ¹/₂ in).
Weight 107 oz.
Provenance: Probably John
Bagwell of Marlefield,
Co.Tipperary.

The design for this imposing urn
was also used at Sèvres where the
model was probably known as
vase Du Barry à guirlandes.
However, since the Sèvres model
dates from 1771, and the urn
from the preceding year, there
must have been a common design
source, probably an engraving,
which is now lost. The engraved
arms are those of Bagwell of
Marlefield, Co.Tipperary, pre-
sumably for John Bagwell (circa
1745-1816), who was Member of
Parliament for County Tipperary
from 1801-1806.

**Rupert Gentle Antiques
The Manor House,
Milton Lilbourne,
Nr. Pewsey,
Wiltshire SN9 5LQ
Tel: 01672-563344
Fax: 01672-564136**

A French 18th-century tortoise-shell and silver-gilt snuff-box, ornamented with gold *piqué* decoration. Circa 1730.
Width 8.3 cm (3 ¼ in).
Depth 6.4 cm (2 ½ in).

The remarkably fine decoration on this box is known as *piqué*, and was produced using a minute drill to insert thousands of tiny gold dots. In this instance, the decoration is in the chinoiserie style.

The Chinese taste was a powerful influence on all aspects of European art and design from the late 16th century until the third quarter of the 18th century. By 1670, chinoiserie was already strongly developed in France, and for the next 60 or 70 years, many designers took their inspiration from the East, partly as a rebellion against the pervading classical tradition in art and letters.

This box exemplifies the height of fashionable design of its time.

**J.H. Bourdon-Smith Ltd.,
24 Mason's Yard,
Duke Street,
St James's,
London SW1Y 6BU
Tel: 0171-839 4714
Fax: 0171-839 3951**

Adam silver - examples of fine piercing: an ensemble of six pierced coasters and a matching boat-shaped bread or fruit basket, with pierced decoration and thread-edge mounts.
William Plummer,
London 1788.
Width (basket) 36.2 cm (14 1/4 in).
Width (smallest coaster)
9.5 cm (3 3/4 in).

Such a set is extremely rare, the smallest coasters being the most unusual of all, their size ideal for a white wine bottle. All the coasters, are engraved with a crest of a griffin's head erased. The boat-shaped basket is engraved with the same crest and the full arms of Camp, Campe, Cotton, Goronee or Quarton impaling Dolseby.

The marks on these pieces are particularly clear, as the set is in near mint condition. The mahogany bases of the coasters are original.

William Plummer, whose workshop was at 47 Gutter Lane, was a prolific maker of fine pierced silver, and he is justly renowned for making sugar and cream baskets and strainers, as well as coasters and a multitude of bread baskets, some earlier examples of which are pierced in the rococo taste.

J.H. BOURDON-SMITH LTD

STAND 75

**J.H. Bourdon-Smith Ltd.,
24 Mason's Yard,
Duke Street,
St James's,
London SW1Y 6BU
Tel: 0171-839 4714
Fax: 0171-839 3951**

Adam silver - examples of fine bright-cut engraving: a pair of covered sauce tureens by Robert Hennell, London 1794; one of a pair of Irish waiters by Thomas Jones, Dublin 1789; and one of a pair of shell-bowl sauce ladles by John Shields, Dublin 1797. Height (tureens) 15.2 cm (6 in).

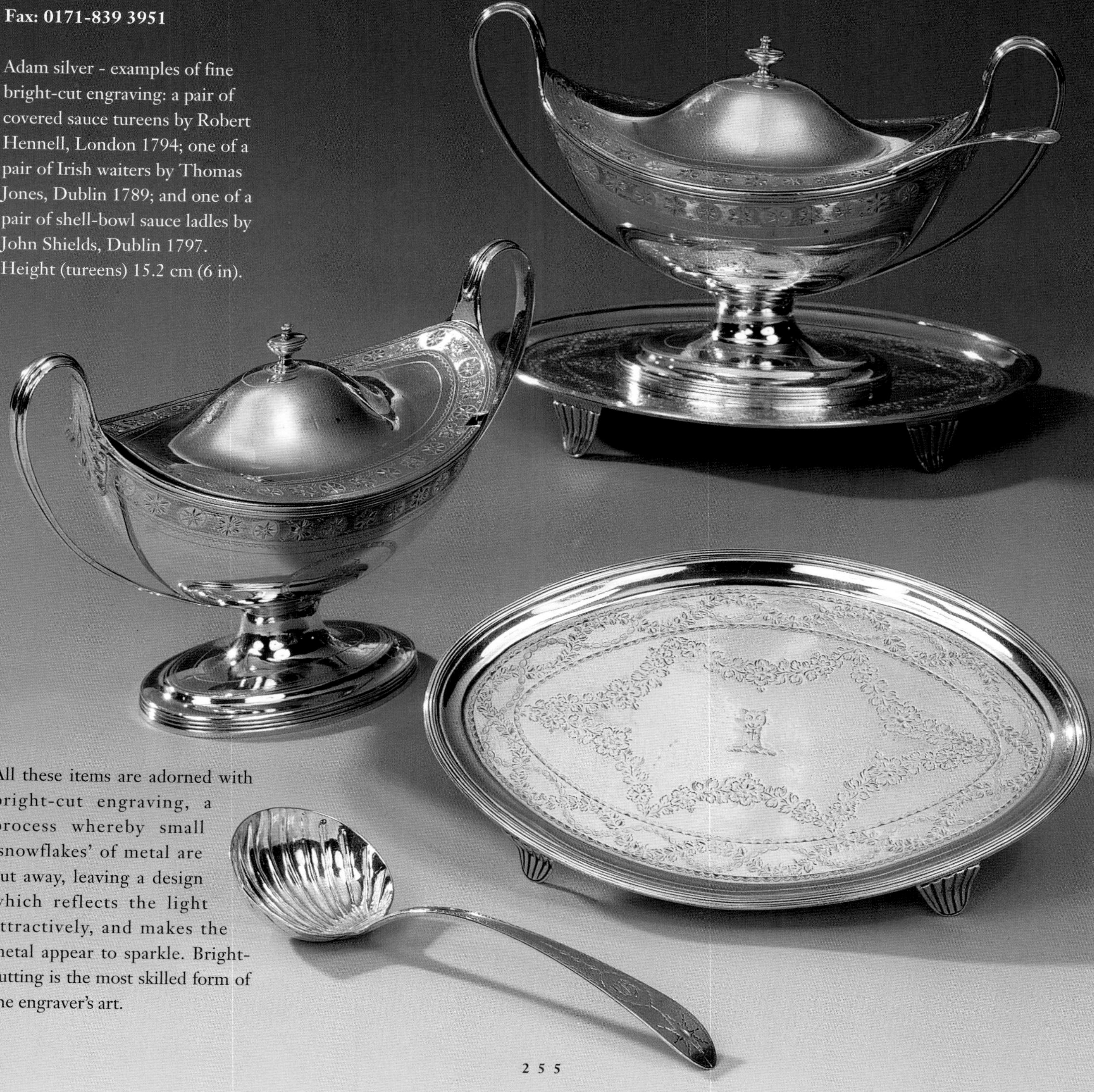

All these items are adorned with bright-cut engraving, a process whereby small 'snowflakes' of metal are cut away, leaving a design which reflects the light attractively, and makes the metal appear to sparkle. Bright-cutting is the most skilled form of the engraver's art.

Halcyon Days,
14 Brook Street,
London W1Y 1AA
and
4 Royal Exchange,
London EC3V 3LL
Tel: 0171-629 8811
Fax: 0171-409 0280

A group of 18th-century English enamel snuff-boxes, each painted with a portrait.

Top left, John Wilkes (1727 - 1797), a politician and journalist who, in 1762, founded a weekly paper, *The North Briton*; the following year he was arrested for libel after publishing in it an attack on the government. He was later elected MP for Middlesex, but was expelled from Parliament. Eventually, after serving as Lord Mayor of London, he was permitted to take his seat as a Member of Parliament in 1774. Length 6 cm (2 ¹/₂ in).

Top right, Edmund Burke (1729 - 1797), Whig statesman and political philosopher who supported free trade and whose portrait was painted by Sir Joshua Reynolds. He advocated peace with America in 1775 - 76, and in 1780 he promoted restrictions on the slave trade. In 1790, he became an impassioned critic of French Revolution democracy, and his strident views were published in *Reflections on the Revolution in France*.

Lower left, John Burgoyne (1722 - 1792), a soldier, dramatist, and politician, otherwise known as 'Gentleman Johnny'. He lived in France from 1751 to 1755, in order to escape his creditors and, in 1776, during military service, he became supreme commander in Canada, surrendering to the Americans at Saratoga in October 1777.

Lower right, Prince Charles Edward, The Young Pretender (1720 - 1788). This portrait of 'Bonnie Prince Charlie' is from an engraving by Robert Strange dated 1745. The grandson of James II, he sought to claim the British throne from the House of Hanover. Following the Battle of Culloden in 1746, he became a fugitive and was helped by Flora MacDonald to escape to France.

Hancocks & Company,
1 Burlington Gardens,
London W1X 2HP
Tel: 0171-493 8904
Fax: 0171-493 8905

A highly versatile suite of jewellery by Van Cleef and Arpels of Paris, comprising a necklace-cum-bracelet and a pair of earrings, the flowers set with bright blue and yellow Ceylon sapphires. The double flower motif may be detached from the necklace and worn as two single clip brooches.
French, circa 1938.

The design for this suite of jewellery was first created by Van Cleef and Arpels in Paris in 1938 and was introduced as '*le passe-partout*'. So popular was the design that it was continued throughout the 1940s and 1950s. In this composite illustration, the necklace and one of the earrings are super-imposed on an advertisement of the period by Van Cleef and Arpels announcing '*le passe-partout - une nouvelle creation*'. The lady in the illustration is shown gazing at the bracelet formed by a rearrangement of the necklace. For other examples of this design, see Sylvia Raulet, *Van Cleef and Arpels*, p. 192 and p. 226, illus.

Hancocks & Company,
1 Burlington Gardens,
London W1X 2HP
Tel: 0171-493 8904
Fax: 0171-493 8905

An unusual antique silver-gilt wine-cooler in the form of the Portland Vase. Philip Rundell, London, 1823.
Height 25 cm (9³⁄₄ in).
Weight 81 oz.

The original Portland Vase, now in the British Museum, was made of cameo glass in Rome, circa 25 BC. It remains one of the most important examples of a glass-blowing technique developed only about 25 years earlier. The base of the vase was originally flat, but having been broken, a replacement plaque was inserted, a feature replicated in this silver-gilt version.

The Portland Vase was discovered outside ancient Rome in 1582. It was sold to Sir William Hamilton in 1783, who in turn sold it the following year to the Dowager Duchess of Portland, whose name it has borne since then. It has been displayed in the British Museum since 1810, and was purchased by them in 1945.

Philip Rundell was appointed Goldsmith and Jeweller to King

George III in 1797, entering a partnership with John Bridge and Edmund Rundell in 1803. Finally, the great silversmith Paul Storr joined the partnership in 1807. On Philip Rundell's death in 1827, his estate was valued at £1.25 million

Hancocks & Company,
1 Burlington Gardens,
London W1X 2HP
Tel: 0171-493 8904
Fax: 0171-493 8905

A magnificent diamond double clip of exceptional quality, comprising over 300 diamonds with a total weight of 29.14 carats, mounted in platinum by Mauboussin of Paris.
Width 8 cm (3¹/₈ in).

The geometric designs of the Art Deco period were applied to diamond clip brooches with great success. This brooch epitomises the double clip in its design, the quality of its diamonds and its manufacture. It was made by the renowned Paris jeweller Mauboussin and, remarkably, is offered for sale in its original case with its first bill of sale, dated 16 October 1939.

The House of Mauboussin originated in 1827, when Messieurs Rocher and Noury established a jewellery shop in Paris. Having joined his uncle, M. Noury, George Mauboussin assumed control of the company in 1896. Mauboussin exhibited at all the major international exhibitions in the first half of this century, and opened branches in London, New York, and Buenos Aires.

In its design and quality, this spectacular jewel exemplifies the finest work of this historic French jeweller.

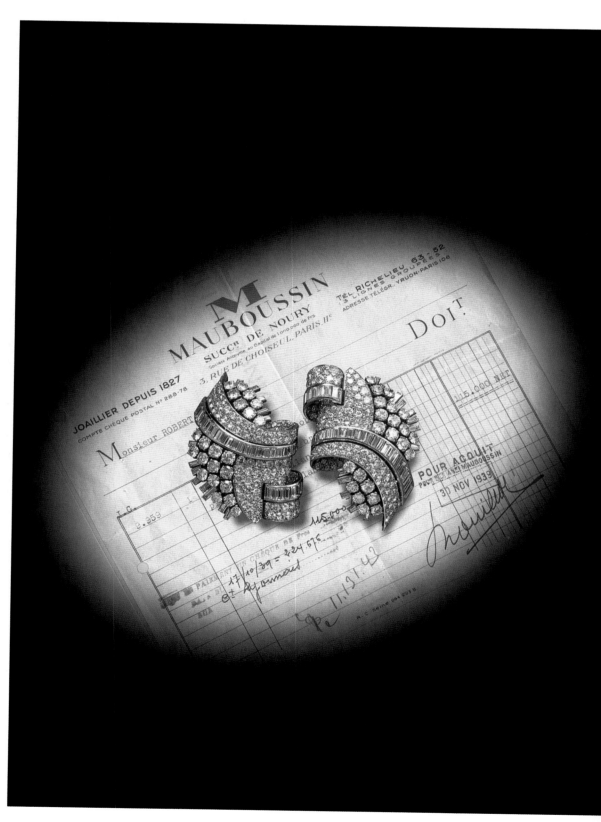

D.S. Lavender (Antiques) Ltd.,
26 Conduit Street,
London W1R 9TA
Tel: 0171-629 1782
Fax: 0171-629 3106

A collection of English and
French jewellery from the 19th
and 20th centuries, dating
between 1880 and 1935.

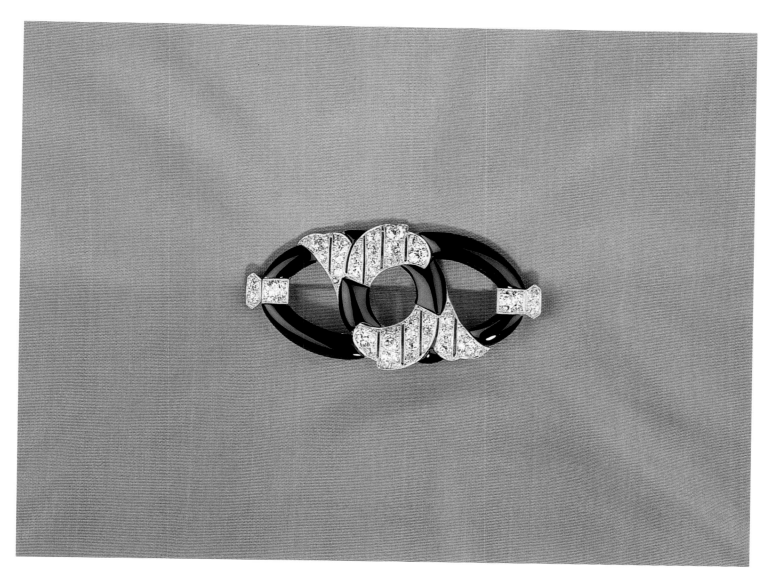

Spink & Son Ltd.,
5 King Street,
St James's,
London SW1Y 6QS
Tel: 0171-930 7888
Fax: 0171-839 4853

An Art Deco black onyx and diamond brooch, by Auger, circa 1925. Length 6 cm (2 ½ in). Width 3 cm (1 ¼ in).

The brooch shown here, with sureté pin fitting, features the classic Art Deco black and white contrast of onyx and diamond with its clearly delineated outline. There is a suggestion of Islamic influence in its closed double arabesque form, terminating in a bifurcated old European-cut diamond-set palmette. Unusually, the reverse is engraved, and the style of this decoration also echoes an Islamic theme.

There is a paucity of information in the literature about a company bearing the name Auger, which operated in the 1920s. It may be a continuation of the firm founded in 1862 by Alphonse Auger and inherited by his son George (b.1864) in 1900. The name is twice impressed on this piece, together with the French control marks. The logo, which is featured inside the lid of the original case, indicates that Auger operated from the Place des Victoires in Paris.

S.J. Phillips Ltd.,
139 New Bond Street,
London W1A 3DL
Tel: 0171-629 6261
Fax: 0171-495 6180

One of a pair of Imari porcelain
pots and covers, the silver
mounts by Paul Leriche,
Paris 1717 - 1722.
Height 22.2 cm (8 ¾ in).

The mounting of oriental
porcelain in silver was a mark of
the high value placed on this rare
commodity. Silver mounts also
served to protect and enhance it.
The fashion for such mounting
reached its height in the period
between 1715 and 1740. The
French silversmith, Paul Leriche,
appears to have specialised in this
practice, for his mark is most
frequently seen on silver mounts.

S.J. Phillips Ltd.,
139 New Bond Street,
London W1A 3DL
Tel: 0171-629 6261
Fax: 0171-495 6180

A set of seven Queen Anne silver casters by Joseph Ward, London 1705. Height of tallest caster 24.1 cm (9 ½ in).

These casters bear the arms of Howe, for Sir James Howe, second Baronet of Cold Barwick or Berwick St Leonard, Wiltshire, (1669 - 1736). A Wiltshire landowner, Sir James inherited the estate on his father's death in 1676, and later served as Member of Parliament for Hindon.

It is rare to find so extensive a set of casters, pairs and three-somes being much more usual.

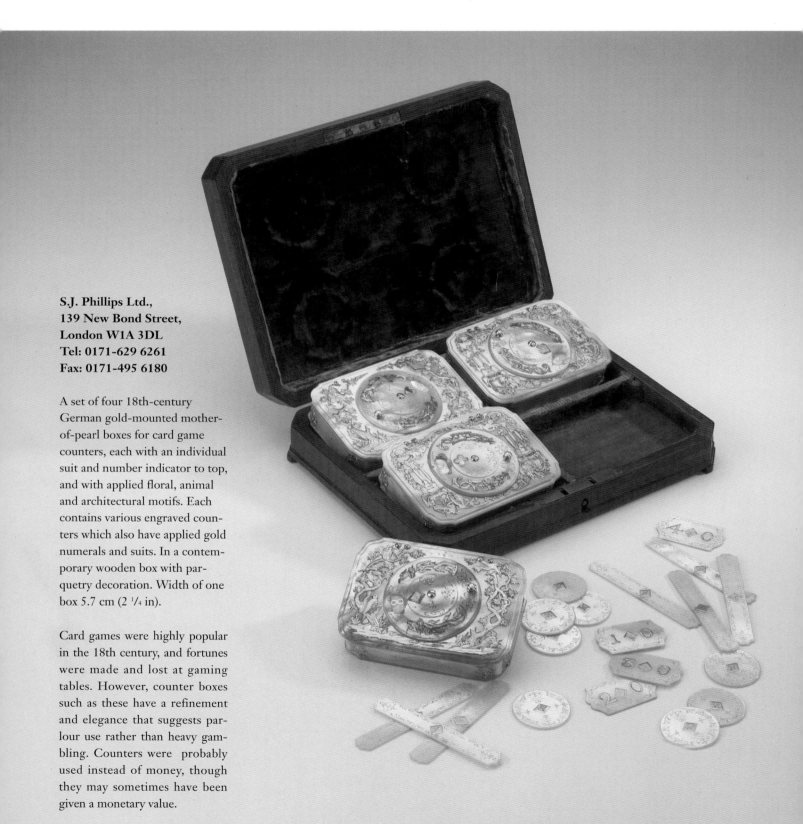

**S.J. Phillips Ltd.,
139 New Bond Street,
London W1A 3DL
Tel: 0171-629 6261
Fax: 0171-495 6180**

A set of four 18th-century German gold-mounted mother-of-pearl boxes for card game counters, each with an individual suit and number indicator to top, and with applied floral, animal and architectural motifs. Each contains various engraved counters which also have applied gold numerals and suits. In a contemporary wooden box with parquetry decoration. Width of one box 5.7 cm (2 ¼ in).

Card games were highly popular in the 18th century, and fortunes were made and lost at gaming tables. However, counter boxes such as these have a refinement and elegance that suggests parlour use rather than heavy gambling. Counters were probably used instead of money, though they may sometimes have been given a monetary value.

S.J. Phillips Ltd.,
139 New Bond Street,
London W1A 3DL
Tel: 0171-629 6261
Fax: 0171-495 6180

A set of five antique diamond circular cluster brooches, all open-set in silver and gold. English, circa 1870. Shown actual size.

These brooches may originally have been made as buttons, or possibly as parts of a hair ornament.

Tadema Gallery,
10 Charlton Place,
London N1 8AJ
Tel. and Fax: 0171-359 1055

An important *Jugendstil* brooch by the German designer Professor Georg Kleemann (1863 - 1932). Gilded silver, *plique à jour*, turquoise, amethyst, garnet and pearl. Circa 1907. Length 12.5 cm (5 in). Width 8.5 cm (3 ¹/₂ in). Literature: *European Jewellery from Historicism to Art Nouveau*, Pforzheim Jewellery Museum, shows a similar jewel executed by Otto Zahn, from the Museum collection, cat. no. 247.

Georg Kleemann studied decorative design in Munich and became a leading German jewellery designer, and professor at the Pforzheim Fachschule from 1887. His book, *Moderner Schmuck*, was published by Birkner & Brecht in 1900, and comprised 100 pages of designs for jewels and haircombs.

Kleemann was not a goldsmith himself, and his unique jewels were executed by Otto Zahn. Other designs were executed by several companies including Theodor Fahrner, Carl Hermann, Victor Mayer and Zerenner.

Tadema Gallery,
10 Charlton Place,
London N1 8AJ
Tel. and Fax: 0171-359 1055

Feuilles d'Automne by the Belgian artist, Philippe Wolfers (1858 - 1929). A highly important gold, *plique à jour*, pearl, and diamond pendant, marked 'PW Ex Unique'. Circa 1902.

Length 5.5 cm (2 ¹/₂ in).
Width 5 cm (2 in).
Literature: Philippe und Marcel Wolfers, *Art Nouveau und Art Deco aus Brussel*, Museum Bellerive, Zurich, 1993, cat. no. 35 (pencil and gouache design, signed 'PW' and dated '10.7.1902', Unikat Werknr. 149).

Philippe Wolfers was a sculptor,

goldsmith and jeweller, whose family firm, Wolfers Frères, Court Jewellers, was founded in 1812 in Brussels. He studied at the Academie Royale des Beaux Arts with the sculptor Isidore de Rudder, and worked in an extravagant French Art Nouveau style. His major series comprised 109 jewels, made between 1897 and 1905, which were marked

'Ex[emplaire] Unique', to distinguish them from the production of the Wolfers firm. Wolfers exhibited at various International Exhibitions including those of Munich in 1898 and 1899, Turin in 1902, Liege in 1905, and Milan in 1906. After 1908, he turned his attention to sculpture.

Gander & White
Shipping Ltd.,
21 Lillie Road,
London SW6 1UE
Tel: 0171-381 0571
Fax: 0171-381 5428
and
33-31 Greenpoint
Avenue,
Long Island City,
N.Y. 11101
U.S.A.
Tel: 718-784 8444
Fax: 718-784 9337
and
24 Rue Lucien
Sampaix,
75010 Paris,
France
Tel: 33-1 42 02 18 92
Fax: 33-1 42 06 33 31

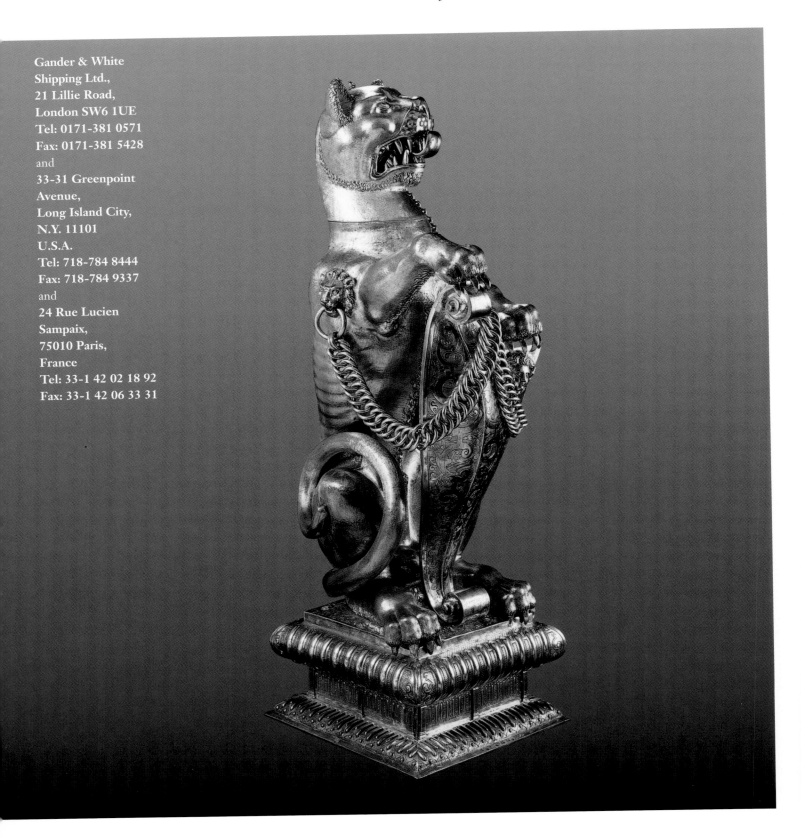

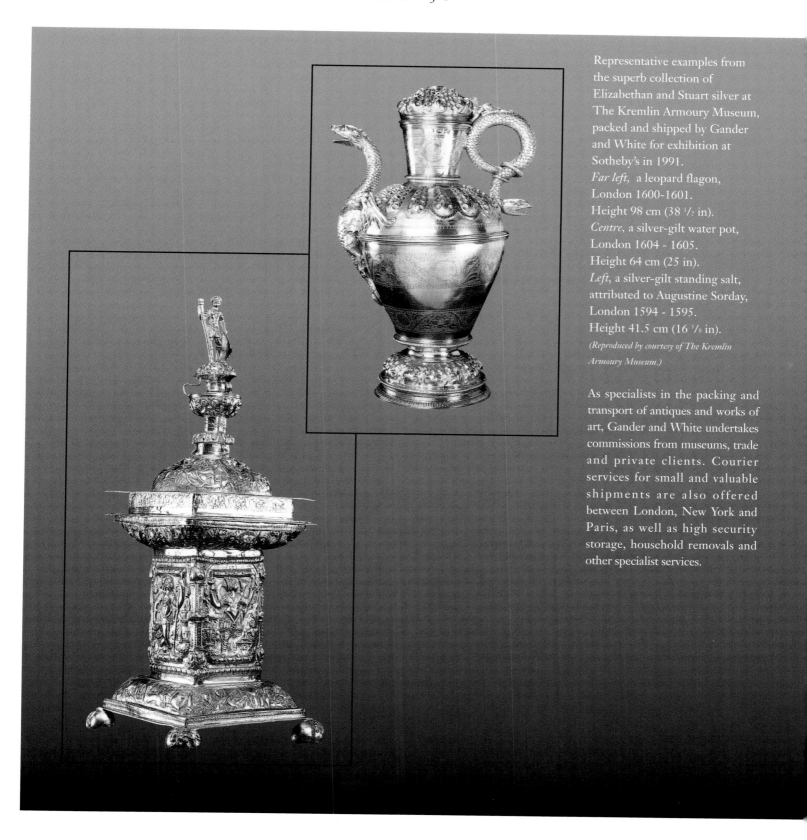

Representative examples from the superb collection of Elizabethan and Stuart silver at The Kremlin Armoury Museum, packed and shipped by Gander and White for exhibition at Sotheby's in 1991.
Far left, a leopard flagon, London 1600-1601. Height 98 cm (38 ¹/₂ in).
Centre, a silver-gilt water pot, London 1604 - 1605. Height 64 cm (25 in).
Left, a silver-gilt standing salt, attributed to Augustine Sorday, London 1594 - 1595. Height 41.5 cm (16 ⁵/₈ in).
(Reproduced by courtesy of The Kremlin Armoury Museum.)

As specialists in the packing and transport of antiques and works of art, Gander and White undertakes commissions from museums, trade and private clients. Courier services for small and valuable shipments are also offered between London, New York and Paris, as well as high security storage, household removals and other specialist services.

END

OF

EXHIBITORS'

SECTION

APPENDICES

BUYING AND SELLING ANTIQUES

By courtesy of Andrew Edmunds

ANTIQUARIANS.
A LA GRECQUE.

WHY BUY?

When it comes to buying antiques, the best advice is timeworn, namely to buy because you are in love with the piece and want to share your life with it for the foreseeable future. Or at least, because you truly want it for itself, feel that the price is affordable to you, and that the piece is worth it.

Buying for investment is not something most dealers like to talk about, believing that such activity belongs in the realms of stockbroking, not art-dealing. Nonetheless, when spending a large sum of money, it is only reasonable to wonder whether it will ultimately be retrievable. No-one can predict the vicissitudes of the art and antiques market, but the best security is found in top quality and fine condition. Though it may seem a contradiction, to spend a little more to attain the finest example is often better than accepting second best for the sake of a few pounds.

People buy antiques for different reasons. A few collectors pursue very specific items, building up precious collections of Japanese sword-guards or Lowestoft eye-baths, while many others aim to furnish a home with everything from pier-glasses and paintings to chaises-longues and chandeliers. Either way, various sources are available to the would-be purchaser.

BUYING FROM A DEALER

There are great advantages to buying from a reputable antique dealer. Those represented in this book are amongst the very best in their chosen fields, and make it their business to seek out the finest art and antiques. Most of them belong to the British Antique Dealers' Association, (BADA), a long-established trade organisation which demands that its members conform to a strict code of conduct. Primarily this benefits the buyer, allowing him to buy with confidence knowing that the dealer guarantees the authenticity of his stock. In the unlikely event that an item proves to be otherwise than as described, the dealer is required, under the rules of membership, to make a full refund.

M. TURPIN
Fine Antiques & Objets d'Art

A pair of George III finely carved giltwood oval Girandoles of large size
– Height: 52 inches (132 cms). Width: 32 inches (81.3 cms).
The design incorporates a Ho Ho bird encircled by tree branches and leaves on the outer border glass,
with the leaves entwining the central mirror frame. English: Circa 1770.

American and French dealers represented in this book belong to their own national equivalent organisations which also demand high standards of integrity from members. In this country there is also LAPADA – The Association of Art and Antique Dealers, and the Society of London Art Dealers (SLAD), which is an association of reputable fine art dealers who undertake to maintain 'fair and honest' standards of dealing. (See page 320 for addresses). All reputable dealers will provide you with a dated, receipted invoice which bears a brief description of the item, including any major restorations or alterations, and the price paid.

The value of cultivating an antique dealer should not be underestimated. Top dealers prize their stock, and will often agree to buy back a piece they have sold some years before, or to exchange it if your requirements change. If you have an interest in one particular area of collecting, the specialist dealer's knowledge and guidance can be invaluable in developing and maintaining your own collection – he can advise you about an object coming up at auction, and may even bid for you (rather than against you) by arrangement.

BUYING AT AN ART AND ANTIQUES FAIR – THE VALUE OF VETTING

Whatever your quarry, you may initially need to visit a number of antique dealers before you find one whose taste coincides with your own. An easy way of doing this without excessive footslogging is to visit a fair, where many dealers are gathered together for a brief period, bringing representative samples of their stock. Antique fairs happen throughout the country and throughout the year, but The Grosvenor House Art & Antiques Fair is the most prestigious of them all. Here you will find some of the finest art and antiques available on the market, together with the leading experts to tell you about them.

Though of course many items have prices which reflect their rarity, this should not intimidate those of more modest funds, for many dealers once consulted can use their contacts to find or direct you to an ideal yet affordable piece.

Even though many of the exhibitors at The Grosvenor House Art & Antiques Fair are amongst the leading experts in their fields, their exhibits are all subjected to independent scrutiny to guarantee their authenticity even further. This process is commonly known as 'vetting', and is rigorously applied to every item, including those which come in later to replenish the stands. The vetting standards are exacting, the criteria precise, and any item which does not meet these must either be relabelled appropriately, or excluded from the Fair. Among the most important criteria are the following:

1. An item must be a genuine antique or work of art of the period that it is represented to be.
2. It must be in its original form and not over restored.
3. It must be properly attributed and correctly labelled ...and dated.

Everyone understands that the passage of time leaves its mark, indeed this can be much of the charm of an antique. Some forms of restoration are therefore permitted, but these are carefully defined and restricted. Nothing that might deceive is allowed in – for example, pieces with additions or alterations to enhance value, 'marriages' of two sections that originally belonged to different pieces, later carving or decoration etc. The list is long and complex, and verbal fisticuffs between exhibitors and 'vetters' are not unknown where so much is a matter of expert opinion. However the overall result is that visitors to The Grosvenor House Art & Antiques Fair can peruse the stands with confidence, knowing that things are, to the experts' best knowledge, as they seem.

BUYING AT AUCTION

This became much more fashionable during the 1980s, as the big auctioneers made a determined effort to attract the

Judith Leiber®

Luxe Jewellery/Minaudieres

Judith Leiber Boutique, Harrods, Knightsbridge: Asprey, 165-169 New Bond Street.

For further information please contact: Judith Leiber (UK) Tel: 0171 416 4160.

public directly. Smart receptions became the necessary social preliminary to the big sales, and everything was done to change the esoteric image of the auction-house to one of approachable, friendly expertise. By thus short-circuiting the system, auctioneers placed dealers directly in competition with their clients. Everyone has now become used to this free-for-all, but before buying at auction it is worth considering one or two points. Auctioneers have many caveats in their small print that protect them against your wrath, should the item sold have defects you had not noticed. Only in the case of a piece being proved a deliberate fake are you likely to get any redress. It is therefore wise to avail yourself of independent expert advice (perhaps from a specialist dealer) before you take the plunge. Another point to remember when calculating your top bid (an essential discipline) is that a 'Buyer's Premium' will be added to the final bid, topped off with VAT (Value Added Tax). Buyer's Premium is an in-house tax charged by most auction houses, and rates vary from 10 per cent upwards, with Sotheby's and Christie's charging 15 per cent on the first £30,000.

VAT AND EXPORTS

If you live outside the European Union and wish to export art and antiques purchased in the United Kingdom, you may be able to reclaim VAT on certain pieces, and you should also be aware of the rules governing exports. The BADA offers advice on both these areas. Detailed information on VAT regulations is available from local VAT offices (under Customs and Excise in the telephone directory). The Department of National Heritage can advise on exports (there are threshold values above which a licence is required to export an antique), and information on the special restrictions on exporting items containing ivory and tortoiseshell (or anything else from endangered species) is available from the Department of the Environment. Addresses are given below.

PACKERS AND SHIPPERS

If you are exporting more than you can carry, you are likely to need the services of a shipper. There are several firms in the UK, many based in or around London, which specialise in packing art and antiques, and shipping them safely to their overseas destinations. However curly and fragile your giltwood mirror or large china vase, it will arrive intact. For information on specialist shippers, contact the BADA.

INDEPENDENT ASSESSMENT OF WORKS OF ART

If you wish to find out about a work of art, there are various sources of information available, ranging from the informal, verbal opinion to a more official written statement. To have an item valued, you can contact either a reputable antique dealer in that field, or a specialist auctioneer. You must make clear the purpose for which you need the valuation – there is a considerable difference between a value based on auction estimate, and the value for which you would be advised to insure the same thing. Expect to pay for a written valuation, though ask in advance how much is charged – it may be a percentage of the value or a flat fee.

Those more interested in other aspects of the work of art – age, origins, type, etc – may find help from a dealer. They may also turn to the major museums and galleries which offer a free consultation service to help with identification, but do not express opinions on value. (See section on Museums and Galleries for further details, page 310.) Another source of information for those who have something they believe to be valuable is the BADA assessment service. The charge for this is £235, for which the BADA will put together a panel of at least three experts who will give a written opinion of the piece, its age, description and authenticity. Contact the BADA for further information.

SELLING

Selling at auction has certain attractions to it - you can hallucinate that the estimate might be wildly exceeded by a couple of determined 'must-have' bidders. However you must bear in mind the many charges that eat into that hammer price, or the cheque which eventually reaches you may seem rather emaciated. These charges include a vendor's commission which may be as much as 15 per cent, though much less for items of high value, and sometimes negotiable. Then there is insurance at 1 per cent of the hammer price, and illustration charges (which can easily run into hundreds). All of these charges attract VAT to boot. Another thing to realise is that you may not get paid for a few weeks after the auction, and even then not unless the buyer has paid the auctioneer.

Selling to a reputable dealer obviates many of these problems. You need to satisfy yourself about the figure you would be happy to accept - you may have shown the item to an auctioneer, or received an independent idea of its sale value from another source. Bear in mind that the dealer needs to make a profit, so do not expect him to pay you the price you see attached to a similar piece in his window. Nonetheless, all good dealers have reputations to preserve, and are constantly hungry for 'good, private stock' – that is, what you have had in your drawing room for the past ten or thirty years. They have every reason to deal fairly with you, and best of all, you receive your money immediately, and with nothing taken out of it.

The final word is, hopefully, unnecessary. That dismal subspecies of the dealing world, known as a 'knocker', must be avoided at all costs. The knocker is an itinerant trader who calls on the gullible (usually the elderly), offering to pay cash for antiques and valuables. Something for nothing is the object of the exercise, and it is extremely unwise to allow such people into your home. Always take proper professional advice – it will save you money.

ADDRESSES

The British Antique Dealers' Association
20 Rutland Gate, London SW7 1BD
(0171-589 4128)

The Grosvenor House Art & Antiques Fair
Organiser's Office, Grosvenor House,
Park Lane, London W1A 3AA
(0171-495 6406 or 0171-499 6363)

Dept. of National Heritage
2-4 Cockspur Street, London SW1Y 5DH
(0171-211 6000)

Dept. of the Environment
Wildlife Trade Licensing Branch, Tollgate House,
Houlton Street, Bristol BS2 9DJ
(0117-987 8202)

Local VAT offices – look under Customs
& Excise in the local telephone directory.

Antiques & Fine Furniture, Third Floor.

Harrods Limited, Knightsbridge, London SW1X 7XL. Telephone 0171-730 1234

John Keil
LIMITED

A fine and rare George III Regency period rosewood centre table, the rectangular top
with inlaid stringing and gilt metal rim, the frieze panelled and with giltwood moulding, the table
raised on black and gilt spiral twist legs with carved acanthus and joined by turned
cross-stretchers, also with carved acanthus, the legs ending in brass castors.
Circa 1810. Height 28 ins (71 cm). Width 54 ins (138 cm). Depth 38½ ins (98 cm).

John Keil

LIMITED

An extremely fine pair of George III Regency period decorated torcheres,
each with a circular top and frieze applied with paterae and anthemia with entrelacs centred by
lion-masks and rings, on triple lion-paw supports carved with acanthus, on concave-sided
triangular base carved with entrelacs, the torcheres raised on ball feet. Circa 1810.
The supports appear to derive from F Primaticcio's 16th Century 'altar-pedestal'
monument for Henri II of France, now in the Louvre
The state bed at Castle Coole, Co Fermanagh has a very similar outline,
also carved with acanthus and with paw feet. See 'English Decorations in
the 18th Century' by Fowler & Cornforth, page 97 fig. 75.
Height 43 ins (110 cm). Diameter 19 ins (49 cm).

154 BROMPTON ROAD · LONDON SW3 1HX · TEL: 0171 589 6454 · FAX: 0171 823 8235

PATRICK JEFFERSON

94 MOUNT STREET
MAYFAIR LONDON W1Y 5HG
TELEPHONE 0171 491 4931 FAX 0171 491 4932

Christopher Bangs

By Appointment Only
P.O. Box 6077. London SW6 7XS

Early metalware and metalwork
and works of art

Telephone: 0171 381 3532
Fax: 0171 381 2192

W. R. Harvey & Co
(Antiques) Ltd.

A rare and magnificent George II Period Mahogany Library Reading Armchair, the horseshoe-shaped
back supporting a ratchet adjusted reading flap with articulated candlestands sliding on a brass rail, the pierced
vase-shaped splat flanked by scrolled supports above a saddle-shaped seat on cabriole legs with
scrolled ear brackets and pad feet with brass castors. Ca 1740.

CARE OF ANTIQUES

As only one in a succession of owners of an antique, you owe it to those that will come after you to take great care of the object during your temporary custodianship. It also behoves you to do so for your own sake, since value and condition are closely linked. Attitudes to the care of antiques have developed over the years as the value of authenticity and original condition have been recognised. Now it is acknowledged that restoration, in the broadest sense, is not always the best course, and every effort should be made at conservation, that is, the preservation of the object in as close to original condition as possible.

Of course restoration has its place, but in the case of valuable antiques much the best advice is to consult a recommended expert in the field – serious damage and loss of value can very easily result from amateur bodging or ill-informed 'improvements'. There are too many stories about fine furniture which has been 'sealed' with spray varnish 'for protection', or invaluable patination on decorative bronzes lost through 'cleaning up' with domestic abrasives. The central principle of professional restoration today is that all processes must be reversible (and therefore carefully recorded).

The following information comprises cautious advice on how to look after different types of antiques. If you are in any doubt, or think that restoration is necessary, then consult a reputable dealer for advice. The British Antique Dealers' Association supports West Dean College in Sussex which offers full-time professional courses on restoration, thus promoting the cause of specialised, highly skilled restoration. Advice on specialist restorers is also available from the Conservation Unit of the Museums and Galleries Commission who will, for a fee of £5, provide a list of five selected restorers in your area. The United Kingdom Institute for Conservation can also advise on finding a specialist restorer from amongst its members. Please see page 320 for these addresses and further useful contacts.

ENVIRONMENTAL FACTORS TO CONSIDER

TEMPERATURE AND HUMIDITY

In the name of comfort we choose to insulate ourselves from the natural environment, centrally heating our houses to a level far removed from the cool damp which our ancestors (and their furniture) endured. Although this keeps us comfortably warm and dry, efficiency dictates that most heating systems come on and off, causing considerable fluctuations in temperature and humidity over a 24 hour period. These fluctuations play havoc with antiques made of organic materials (most obviously wooden furniture), causing movement as the material swells to absorb moisture and shrinks as it dries out again. Under such conditions, wood may warp or split. Ideally you should aim for as constant a temperature as possible, maintain humidity levels using a carefully adjusted humidifier, and keep furniture well away from sources of heat.

LIGHT

The other major enemy of antiques is light, in particular its ultra-violet component which breaks down organic materials. This is why you find so many stately homes plunged in Stygian gloom, with blinds at the windows allowing only the minimum light by which to peer at their fragile treasures. If you cannot face living in such crepuscular conditions, at least keep your antiques out of direct sunlight, and consider using blinds when the room is not in use. Bear in mind that carpets and curtains are especially vulnerable to light damage. Blinds will help the latter while you should turn carpets round regularly to allow even exposure. Prolonged exposure to daylight even without direct sun is also damaging, and precautions should be taken to protect antiques.

Barry Davies Oriental Art Ltd

A Kakiemon porcelain model of an Indian elephant, decorated in black, blue,
green, iron-red and yellow enamels.
Height 33.5 cms. Circa 1680.
An Exhibition of Japanese Porcelain from the Collection of Dr Oliver Impey
will be held at our Gallery from 17-27 June 1997. A fully illustrated
Catalogue will be available.

1 Davies Street Mayfair London W1Y 1LL   Telephone 0171 408 0207   Fax 0171 493 3422

INFESTATION

Although furniture from respectable sources is most unlikely to be affected, it is good practice to check newly acquired pieces before installing them in your home, lest unwanted passengers are present. Woodworm, which is the larva of the furniture beetle, chews its way through timber, finally launching itself in the summer and flying off to lay more eggs in the next tasty piece of wood. It prospers in the still air of closed rooms and attics, presenting less of a hazard in the normal environment where air circulates freely. Regular inspections for fresh holes and tell-tale sawdust are, however, a wise precaution, followed where necessary by prompt treatment with a recommended insecticide (carefully avoiding any polished surface).

CARE OF FURNITURE

The damaging effects of temperature fluctuations and light have already been mentioned. Patina is the word used to describe the veneer of age that the best antique furniture has developed over a long period – it is a combination of appropriate wear and genteel grime that produces a lustrous finish and is not fakeable, and is therefore much esteemed. At all costs this must be preserved, and the best way of doing this is to combine infrequent and sparing applications of good beeswax-based polish (twice a year is sufficient for most pieces), with frequent dustings using a soft cloth and elbow grease. Spray polishes should not be used on antique furniture, since the silicon in them causes a sticky residue to build up, and the high proportion of spirit may desiccate some of the natural oils. Cream polishes should not be used on veneered furniture, as moisture from the cream may creep under the veneer and start to loosen it. On the subject of veneer, always be sure to keep any small pieces which come off, and present them to your restorer along with the piece of furniture, to save him the labour of finding matching replacements.

Give your antique furniture the care you might lavish on a much-loved elderly relative, sparing it the stresses and strains of rough, inconsiderate handling. Just as you would not ask your ancient aunt to stand on one leg while holding a heavy load, do not expect your antique chairs to survive long if you or your guests habitually tilt them back onto two legs. Likewise, the fall-fronts of bureaux should always be supported on both bearers, and both handles used when opening drawers (beeswax on the sides will ease stiff drawers). Empty furniture before moving it so that it can be lifted, not dragged. Lift tables by the frame, not the top, and chairs by the seat. Gentle buffing with a soft cloth is all that brass furniture mounts (handles etc) require as they should not be too bright. Even this should not be done to ormolu mounts as the gilded surface is so fragile – a soft brush to remove dust is enough.

Giltwood furniture and mirrors need particular care. Water-based gilding, used particularly in the 18th century, remains susceptible to moisture, so must only be dusted with a soft, dry brush. Oil-based gilding, more commonly used in the 19th century, is more robust, and may be gently wiped down. Never use gold paint to disguise chips – it will be hideously obvious. It is better to use a filler and little ochre watercolour if you must, but much wiser to consult a restorer.

CARE OF CERAMICS

Modern domestic aids were not designed with antiques in mind – do not microwave your dinner on your Derby plate (or anything else), and do not even warm your antique plates in the oven. Likewise, nothing in this category should ever be put in a dishwasher – the powder, the temperature, and the vibration all pose threats to delicate porcelain and pottery. Instead, wash porcelain one piece at a time, with great care, in lukewarm water with a little detergent. If the piece is repaired, cracked or riveted, do not submerge, but gently wipe clean. The last instruction applies also to pottery such as faience and majolica which should not be submerged. Dusting with a soft paintbrush should suffice for porcelain figures where complex flower or leaf-work makes them particularly fragile. Support the largest part when handling porcelain or pottery – handles are not to be relied upon, and be aware that a loose lid may fly off as you pick the piece up, unless held in place. Never use adhesive tape to secure lids as it can stain, and also effortlessly removes precious gilding. If a piece does get broken, salvage every scrap and speed along to the restorer before fiddling around wondering whether you could glue it yourself. Proper sticking is a skilled job and most successfully performed with fresh, clean edges to work with.

CARE OF GLASS

Most antique glass can be safely washed by hand in water with a little detergent, and dried with a lint-free cloth. Glass with enamel or gilt decoration requires extra care as the

IMPORTANT
ENGLISH FURNITURE

This set of fourteen George III mahogany dining-chairs was supplied to Daniel Lascelles (d. 1784) for Goldsborough Hall, Yorkshire by Thomas Chippendale. They were first sold in 1976 for £10,450, and then again in July 1996 for £859,500, not only becoming the most expensive set of dining-chairs ever sold at auction, but also the most expensive lot of English furniture sold at auction in 1996; both these sales were at Christie's. They were purchased by the Metropolitan Museum of Art, New York for the Lansdowne House Dining-Room which was installed in the Museum in 1954. It is known from inventories that the Lansdowne dining-room originally housed a set of fourteen chairs of this model by Chippendale.

Please contact Robert Copley on (0171) 389 2353

CHRISTIE'S

8 King Street, St. James's, London SW1Y 6QT Tel: (0171) 839 9060 Fax: (0171) 389 2225 Internet: http://www.christies.com

decoration is fragile. Ancient glass with a flaking, iridescent surface should be handled as little as possible, and not washed. Decanters can be cleaned inside using a solution of denture cleaner in warm water, or with vinegar. Leave either in the decanter for about 24 hours, drain, rinse and allow to dry without the stopper in. Gentle dusting will keep most chandeliers sparkling, but if you must go further, photograph the chandelier from several angles as a record before removing any drops, and make sure you will be able to work out how to reassemble it correctly. Drops may then be removed, washed in warm water, dried and replaced.

CARE OF SILVER AND METALWARE

Abrasive cleaners erode the surface of silver, the effect of which may be seen where silver has been assiduously cleaned every week or so, and engraved decoration has been reduced to a ghostly shadow as a result. If only slightly dirty, silver, silver plate and Sheffield plate benefit from washing in soap and water and buffing with a soft cloth. Where an object contains sections of iron or steel (e.g. candlesticks), care should be taken that these areas do not get wet. For heavier tarnish on fine silver, top experts recommend a mixture of rouge and white chalk, mixed with water and applied with cotton wool. This both cleans and helps to develop patination. Good silversmiths should be able to supply these materials on request. Gentle use of a soft brush in areas of chased or cast ornament will help to keep these clean. Felt bags help stored silver stay clean, and also help to protect it from scratching and denting. Do not use the dishwasher, especially for plated cutlery. The use of polishes which deposit a thin layer of silver onto base metal has become widespread on tired, balding silver plate, which then turns up in markets looking suspiciously bright. Use of such a product on antique Sheffield plate devalues the item.

Antique brass and copper should also be subjected to the minimum of abrasive treatment, and regular buffing with a soft cloth is the best way of keeping it clean. The glowing, soft brown patination on some early brass and copper should never be treated with abrasives – a touch of furniture wax protects it and keeps it lustrous. In particular instances where the brass was originally lacquered – for example brass carriage clocks and scientific instruments – the lacquer acquires its own aged look which is valued. Such items should on no account be polished with abrasives to achieve a bright appearance.

CARE OF PAINTINGS, WATERCOLOURS AND PRINTS

These should be hung securely on a wall away from direct heat, sunlight, and any damp. It is beneficial to have air circulating around a picture, so allow it to hang away from the wall at the top, and, on an exterior wall, it is advisable to insulate it at the lower edge, perhaps using a slice from a cork. Flaking or lifting paint and discoloured varnish on oil paintings are all indications that a professional restorer should be sought. Be aware that picture lights may create hot-spots on a painting's surface leading to damage. Ideally, minimise the use of picture lights, or use the special cool bulbs which are available.

Works on paper, watercolours, drawings and prints, are particularly fragile, and vulnerable to light and damp. The latter can cause brown spots known as foxing. This can usually be rectified, but ensure that the work is done by a trained and accredited paper conservator. Special glass may be fitted to protect drawings from fading, but the simplest advice is to keep these works in the lowest light conditions acceptable. Works on paper should be mounted on acid-free board. The sealing at the back of frames should be regularly checked to minimise the chance of invasion by thunderflies – not in themselves destructive, but unsightly and tiresome.

CARE OF TEXTILES AND CARPETS

Light causes fading and deterioration of fibres, and is the chief enemy of textiles. There are also inherent weaknesses in some embroidered fabrics – for example, the precious metal thread used in many grand state bed hangings, or in some court dresses, can by its sheer weight over the years, destroy the silk on to which it was sewn. This demonstrates the importance of adequately supporting hanging textiles, so the weight is evenly distributed. Samplers and embroidered pictures should not be mounted on stretchers, but on fabric-covered, acid-free board, and framed with air-space between the surface and the glass. Items which are not displayed should be wrapped in acid-free white tissue, and loosely rolled to avoid creasing. Mothballs may be used, but keep them well insulated from contact with the textile itself.

Carpets and rugs should be insulated from the floor and supported using an underlay of exactly the right size. Choose their location wisely, to minimise wear, and regularly turn them round to even out the effects of direct light. It is not a good idea to allow furniture to rest on an antique carpet, as this tends to impose localised strains and cause wrinkling, both of which can do damage. If furniture must rest on the carpet, for example in a dining room, use pads or cups on the furniture feet to protect the carpet, and have a good, thick, non-slip underlay. Keep carpets free of dust by vacuuming (with the pile), using a hand-held vacuum cleaner rather than the upright variety (which has a voracious appetite for loose fringes). Look out for any unravelling fringes or edges, as well as holes, and have these treated promptly by an expert, as leaving them to get worse will be much more expensive. Take expert advice about washing a carpet – colours can run, and you can do untold damage with a bottle of carpet cleaner and your hosepipe.

CARE OF CLOCKS

Antique clocks benefit from being kept wound. When adjusting the hands, move them in a clockwise direction only, allowing the clock time to strike each hour as you go past. There are many 'fixers' around who will do a bodge job on a clock, and the wise course is to find a qualified horologist to carry out any further adjustments or repairs.

CARE OF JEWELLERY

Antique jewellery should not be subjected to domestic duties as it is not strong enough and prone to damage. Even gemstones can crack if subjected to a blow or to a sudden change in temperature, and soft organic materials like pearl or ivory are very vulnerable to their environment. Apply perfume before putting on jewellery, rather than after, since the alcohol in it is potentially damaging. Jewellery should not be jumbled together, but each item kept in a separate box, to avoid damage. Keep jewellery dust free with a soft brush and buff with a chamois leather. Check settings regularly to ensure their security. Any further work should be left to a qualified jeweller.

CARE OF SCULPTURE AND STATUARY

Garden statuary, especially of marble and stone, is vulnerable to the weather. Most destructive is the freezing of water within the crystalline structure of natural materials. For protection, vulnerable pieces should be covered during the winter, as at Versailles, where sentry boxes are placed around the statuary. If covering is not possible, delicate sculpture should be moved to a conservatory. The more durable mediums for garden ornament include lead, bronze, iron and the paler terracottas like Coadestone, and these are comparatively maintenance free. All containers, however, including vases and fountain bowls, must be drained for the winter to prevent damage by ice, and drainage holes kept clear.

The patination of indoor sculpture, bronze in particular, is valuable, and cleaning should be limited to dusting, unless expert advice has been taken.

SECURITY

This is an area of care which should concern every owner of fine antiques who does not wish to come home and find that an unbidden removal lorry has driven off with his treasures, from silver to carpets and even heavy furniture. Security systems in the home are obviously essential, but so too are regular, professional valuations for insurance purposes. It is not enough to keep old invoices for years and add on ten per cent occasionally when you think of it. Values can change fast, and only a professional can keep you up to date. The BADA will advise on valuations, as will good auctioneers. Expect to pay for a full, written valuation, but regard this as highly sensible protection of your investment.

The police find photographic records a useful adjunct to full descriptions with measurements, so have all your antiques photographed, or consider a video record. Valuations and photographic records should of course be securely kept, preferably under lock and key and away from the home, or they will provide a useful shopping list for the burglar. Another way of securing your possessions, or at least making them more readily recoverable, is to mark them with a security marker pen, available from DIY stores. Choose the least conspicuous area of the underside, and write your postal code, followed by the number of your house, or the first two letters of the house name.

Crowther
OF SYON LODGE
— LONDON —

Busch Corner, London Road
Isleworth, Middlesex TW7 5BH
England
Tel: 0181-560 7978
Fax: 0181-568 7572

Ossowski

A pair of gessowork looking-glasses in the manner of William Kent. English. Circa 1740.

| 57" | tall | 145cm |
| 31" | wide | 79cm |

A Pair of Mahogany Library Armchairs, George II, circa 1745, in the manner of **Giles Grendey**. Sold for £ 166,500 ($ 259,740) at Sotheby's London on 5th July 1996.

An Anglo-Russian Blue John and Gilt-bronze-muonted Vase, third quarter 18th Century, in the manner of **Matthew Boulton**. Sold for £ 205,000 ($ 342,350) at Sotheby's London on 15th November 1996.

A Pair of Carved Mahogany Armchairs, George III, circa 1760, attributed to **William Vile**. Sold for £ 837,500 ($ 1,306,500) at Sotheby's London on 5th July 1996.

A Pair of Giltwood Girandoles, George III, circa 1765, in the manner of **John Linnell**. Sold for $ 173,000 (£ 106,135) at Sotheby's New York in October 1996.

OUTSTANDING
ENGLISH FURNITURE
AT SOTHEBY'S

A Pair of Mahogany and Gilt-brass-mounted Commodes, George III, circa 1770, attributed to **John Linnell**. Sold for £ 276,500 ($ 431,340) at Sotheby's London on 5th July 1996.

An Oak and Ebony-inlaid Four Pillar Dining Table, Regency, circa 1815, attributed to **George Bullock**. Sold for £ 232,500 ($ 388,275) at Sotheby's London on 15th November 1996.

A Walnut, **Burr Walnut**, Brass-mounted and Brass-inlaid Bureau Bookcase, circa 1730. Sold for $ 310,500 (£ 190,490) at Sotheby's New York on 12th December 1996.

A Pair of Giltwood Armchairs, George III, circa 1760. Sold for $ 178,500 (£ 117,810) at Sotheby's New York in April 1996.

SOTHEBY'S
Founded 1744

34-35 New Bond Street, London W1A 2AA, tel: (0171) 408 5470
1334 York Avenue, New York, NY 10021, tel: (212) 606 7577

LORIN LILTI

A late 18ᵗʰ century satinwood bookcase. English circa 1790

Width	5' 5 ½"	(167 cm)
Depth	11½"	(29 cm)
Height	7' 11½	(243 cm)

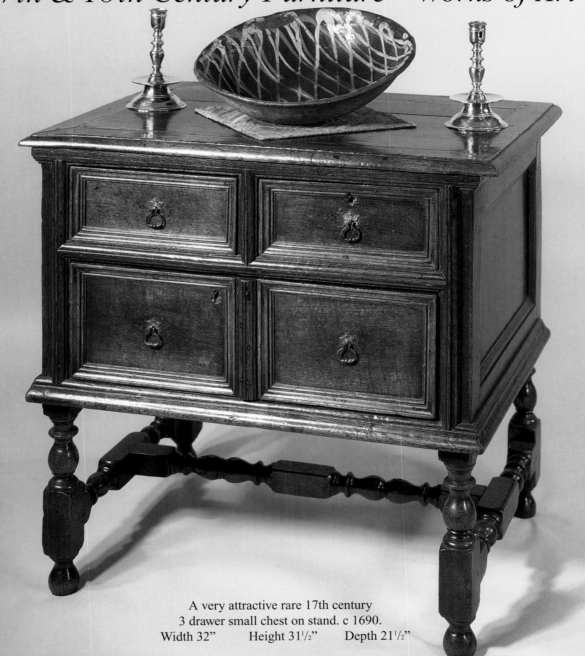

COUNTRY LIFE
CENTENARY
1897 - 1997

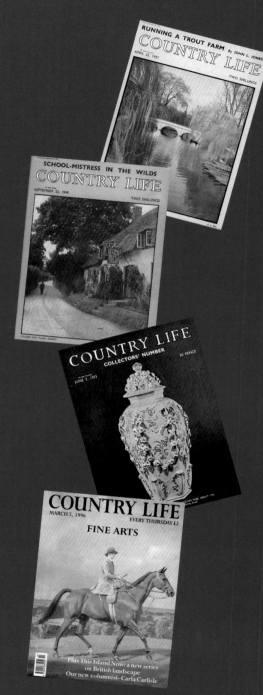

Subscriptions: £108 for 51 issues, £54 for 26. To order: Write to Country Life Subscriptions,
FREEPOST CY1061, Haywards Heath, West Sussex RH16 3ZA
enclosing a cheque or credit card details or telephone: 01444 445555
Overseas rates on application.

IPC Magazines Ltd., King's Reach Tower, Stamford Street, London SE1 9LS

*Frederick Goodall, R.A., (1822 - 1904), 'At the Well', oil on canvas,
signed & dated 1864, 108 x 71.5 cm. Estimate: £20,000 - £30,000
To be sold on Thursday 12 June 1997*

Fine 19th Century European Paintings

Enquiries: Charles O'Brien or Alistair Laird ~ 0171 393 3960
Catalogue Enquiries: Helen Grantham ~ 0171 393 3933

BONHAMS
—— AUCTIONEERS & VALUERS SINCE 1793 ——

Montpelier Street, London SW7 1HH. Tel: 0171 393 3900 Fax: 0171 393 3905 Internet: http://www.Bonhams.com/

PERIODS AND STYLES

REIGNING MONARCHS 1558-1910

Elizabeth I	1558 - 1603
James I	1603 - 1625
Charles I	1625 - 1649
Commonwealth	1649 - 1660
Charles II	1660 - 1685
James II	1685 - 1688
William & Mary (Mary d.1694)	1689 - 1702
Anne	1702 - 1714
George I	1714 - 1727
George II	1727 - 1760
George III	1760 - 1820
(Regency	1811 - 1820)
George IV	1820 - 1830
William IV	1830 - 1837
Victoria	1837 - 1901
Edward VII	1901 - 1910
George V	1910 - 1936
Edward VIII	1936
George VI	1936 - 1952
Elizabeth II	1952-

GUIDE TO BRITISH STYLES AND PERIODS

Gothic	16th century and earlier
Baroque	circa 1620 - 1700
Puritan	mid 17th century
Rococo (with Chinoiserie and Gothic)	circa 1730 - 1760
Neo-classical	circa 1760 - 1800
Empire	circa 1800 - 1815
Regency	circa 1800 - 1830
Victorian eclecticism including revivals of Rococo, Gothic, Japonaiserie	circa 1830 - 1900
Arts and Crafts and Aesthetic Movement	circa 1880 - 1900
Art Nouveau and Liberty style	circa 1890 - 1920
Art Deco	circa 1920 - 1940
Modern Movement	from circa 1940

FRENCH REIGNS AND PERIODS

Louis XIII	1610 - 1643
Louis XIV	1643 - 1715
Régence	1715 - 1723
Louis XV	1723 - 1774
Louis XVI	1774 - 1793
Directoire	1793 - 1799
Empire	1799 - 1815
Restauration	1815 - 1830
(Louis XVIII to 1824; Charles X to 1830)	
Louis-Philippe	1830 - 1848
Second Empire	1848 - 1870
Third Republic	1871 - 1940

VERDURA

PRINCIPAL CHINESE DYNASTIES

Shang . . . . 16th to 11th century BC

Western Zhou . . . . 11th century to 770 BC

Eastern Zhou . . . . 770 - 256 BC

Warring States . . . . 453 - 221 BC

Qin . . . . 221 - 206 BC

Han . . . . 206 BC - AD 220

The Six Dynasties . . . . 220 - 580

Sui . . . . 581 - 618

Tang . . . . 618 - 907

The Five Dynasties . . . . 907 - 960

Liao . . . . 916 - 1125

Northern Song . . . . 960 - 1127

Jin . . . . 1115 - 1234

Southern Song . . . . 1127 - 1279

Yuan . . . . 1279 - 1368

Ming . . . . 1368 - 1644

Qing . . . . 1644 - 1911

REIGNS DURING MING AND QING DYNASTIES

MING

Hongwu . . . . 1368 - 1398

Yongle . . . . 1403 - 1424

Xuande . . . . 1426 - 1435

Chenghua . . . . 1465 - 1487

Hongzhi . . . . 1488 - 1505

Zhengde . . . . 1506 - 1521

Jiajing . . . . 1522 - 1566

Longqing . . . . 1567 - 1572

Wanli . . . . 1573 - 1619

Tianqi . . . . 1621 - 1627

Chongzhen . . . . 1628 - 1644

QING

Shunzhi . . . . 1644 - 1661

Kangxi . . . . 1662 - 1722

Yongzheng . . . . 1723 - 1735

Qianlong . . . . 1736 - 1795

Jiaqing . . . . 1796 - 1820

Daoguang . . . . 1821 - 1850

Xianfeng . . . . 1851 - 1861

Tongzchi . . . . 1862 - 1874

Guangxu . . . . 1875 - 1908

Zuantong . . . . 1909 - 1912

Hongxian 1916

The *Lord of the Isles*

The *Lord of the Isles* has been designed in conjunction with the Prince of Wales
and is taken from the green and cream Scottish hunting tartan, Lord of the Isles, a title
His Royal Highness inherited upon becoming heir to the throne.

Thomas Goode offers the finest selection of china, glass and silverware in the world.

THOMAS GOODE

SINCE 1827

KESHISHIAN
Antique Carpets, Tapestries & Aubussons

A rare set of **three** Charles X Aubusson carpets, French c1825.
A pair 17ft 5in x 13ft 8in : 530cm x 412cm and another 23ft 5in x 17ft 7in : 714cm x 535cm.

Provenance: The Estate of the late First Lord Brocket, Brocket Hall, Welwyn, Hertfordshire.

73 PIMLICO ROAD, LONDON SW1W 8NE   TELEPHONE 0171-730 8810   FACSIMILE 0171-730 8803

FINE FURNITURE AT PHILLIPS

A George III mahogany Breakfront Library Bookcase, 2.29m wide, 2.46m high.
Provenance : Chestham Park, Henfield, Sussex, from the properties of Mrs Nora Prince-Littler and the late Prince-Littler C.B.E.
Estimate : £10,000-£15,000

To be sold on 17th June 1997
This sale is currently on view at Phillips, 101 New Bond Street

For further information or specific viewing times please contact
Michael Cowley or Jonathan Cook, tel : (0171) 468 8321

http://www.phillips-auctions.com

LONDON

Phillips
INTERNATIONAL
AUCTIONEERS & VALUERS

101 New Bond Street, London W1Y 0AS

The marquetry top of the Basildon Park caryatid table. The National Trust.
Photo: Geremy Butler. Discussed in an article by Eileen Harris 'Imposing puzzles at Basildon House',
Apollo April 1997. A special issue in collaboration with The National Trust.

FRANÇOIS LÉAGE

Important 18th-century French furniture

178, Faubourg Saint-Honoré · 75008 PARIS
Tél: 01-45 63 43 46 et 01-45 63 82 46 · Fax: 01-42 56 46 30

PICKETT
FINE LEATHER

Ostrich and crocodile purses and wallets available
from a wide selection of colours and styles.

Box calf handbag by Launer.

Bench made bridle small leathergoods
by Andrew Soos.

Double decker travel bag
by Tanner Krolle.

Kelly bags shown in pigskin and lizard. Also
available in calf, ostrich and crocodile in a variety
of colours. From £225 by Wigmore.

Traditional lid over base attachés
by Papworth from £415.

Soft overnight bags with shoulder straps
by Regent Belt from £120.

Pashmina shawls (210cms x 98cms)
from a selection of over forty colours at £195.

Tusting leather overnight bag, £275.

41 BURLINGTON ARCADE LONDON W1V 9AE   TEL: 0171-493 8939   FAX: 0171-629 3836
149 SLOANE STREET LONDON SW1X 9BZ   TEL: 0171-823 5638   FAX: 0171-730 0299

DANIEL KATZ LTD

European Sculpture & Works of Art
Old Master Paintings

A white marble vase depicting
The graces binding cupid with a chain of roses

Signed A THORWALDSEN. INV.

Rome C. 1835

Height: 200 cms

Provenance: John W. Merriam, USA

59 Jermyn Street, London SW1Y 6LX

Tel: 0171 493 0688 Fax: 0171 499 7493

NEW INTERNET SITE http://www.katz.co.uk

e-mail: danny@katz.co.uk

LONDON MUSEUMS AND PUBLIC GALLERIES

Barbican Art Gallery
Gallery Floor, Barbican Centre, Silk Street,
EC2Y 8DB (0171-638 4141 ext.7619).
Regular art exhibitions.

Bethnal Green Museum of Childhood
Cambridge Heath Road, E2 9PA
(0181-980 3204).
*One of the largest displays of toys and childhood
paraphernalia in the world, including dolls, dolls' houses,
and the social history of childhood.*

British Museum
Great Russell Street, WC1B 3DG (0171-636 1555).
*The national collection of pre-historic and ancient
artefacts (including Greek, Roman, Egyptian, Romano-
British), as well as prints and drawings, coins and
medals, Oriental works of art and medieval works.*

Courtauld Institute Galleries
Somerset House, Strand, WC2R 0RN
(0171-873 2526).
*Famous French Impressionist and Post-Impressionist art
from the Courtauld Collection, as well as much other
European art from 14th to 20th centuries.*

Crafts Council
44a Pentonville Road, Islington, N1 9BY
(0171-278 7700).
*National centre for crafts, offering information and
regular exhibitions.*

Dulwich Picture Gallery
College Road, SE21 7AD (0181-693 5254).
*Fine display of Old Master paintings including Van
Dyck, Rubens, Rembrandt, Poussin, Claude, Murillo as
well as Gainsborough, Hogarth and Lawrence.*

The Fan Museum
12 Croom's Hill, Greenwich, SE10 8ER
(0181-858 7879).
*Museum devoted entirely to fans and their history,
featuring a superb private collection, and holding regular
special exhibitions.*

Geffrye Museum
Kingsland Road, Shoreditch E2 8EA
(0171-739 9893).
*Eighteenth century almshouses containing collections of
furniture, decorative arts and paintings arranged in a
series of period rooms.*

Kenwood
The Iveagh Bequest, Hampstead Lane, NW3
(0181-348 1286).
*A Robert Adam mansion containing an important
collection of paintings including Vermeer, Frans Hals and
Rembrandt, and fine British 18th and early 19th
century painting including Gainsborough, Reynolds,
Romney and Turner. Also fine neo-classical furniture.*

Leighton House Art Gallery and Museum
12 Holland Park Road, Kensington,
W14 8LZ (0171-602 3316).
*Home of Frederick, Lord Leighton, displaying his
own painting and sculpture, as well as work by Millais,
Watts and Burne Jones. His collection of Islamic tiles are
displayed to great effect on the walls of the Arab Hall.*

Linley Sambourne House
18 Stafford Terrace, W8 7BH (0181-994 1019)
*Late 19th century interior almost unchanged from the
time of its first owner, complete with original decoration,
furniture and pictures.*

Marble Hill House
Richmond Road, Twickenham (0181-892 5115).
*Perfect example of an English Palladian villa containing
early Georgian paintings and furniture.*

Museum of London
London Wall, EC2Y 5HN (0171-600 0807).
A wide-ranging collection of material reflecting London's development from earliest times, including fine and decorative arts as well as everyday objects, maps, ephemera, vehicles and costume.

National Gallery
Trafalgar Square, WC2N 5DN (0171-839 3321).
The nation's superb permanent collection of Western painting from the 13th to 20th centuries, including Leonardo, Rembrandt, Constable and Picasso – in fact there can be few Western artists of repute not represented here. The Sainsbury wing houses the early Renaissance collection. Also temporary exhibitions.

National Maritime Museum
including the Royal Observatory and the Queen's House, Romney Road, Greenwich SE10 9NF (0181-858 4422).
The museum collection reflects many aspects of maritime history, with paintings, prints and charts, naval memorabilia, and works of art relevant to the sea or to sea-going men. The painting collection is especially distinguished. The history of astronomy is well represented. A special Nelson exhibition is now a permanent feature.

National Portrait Gallery
St Martin's Place, WC2H 0HE (0171-306 0055).
The faces of the great and the good in British life are represented here in paintings, drawings, prints and photographs making a fascinating collection ranging from Tudor miniatures by Hilliard to the Princess of Wales.

Osterly Park House
Isleworth, TW7 4RB (0181-560 3918).
Eighteenth century villa featuring elegant neo-classical decoration and furniture designed by Robert Adam.

Percival David Foundation of Chinese Art
53 Gordon Square, WC1H 0PD (0171-387 3909).
Extensive collection of early Chinese ceramics and a large reference library on Chinese art.

The Queen's Gallery
Buckingham Palace Road, SW1 (0171-493 3175).
Part of Buckingham Palace housing exhibitions from March to December featuring works of art in the Royal Collection.

Royal Academy of Arts
Burlington House, Piccadilly, London W1V 0DS (0171-439 7438).
Major loan exhibitions throughout the year, and 'Summer Exhibition' of living artists' work.

Royal Armouries
Tower of London, EC3N 4AB (0171-480 6358).
Arms and armour from the time of Henry V to Edward VIII.

Spencer House
27 St James's Place, SW1 (0171-409 0526).
The finest surviving private palace, built 1756-66 for the first Earl Spencer, recently renovated and reopened.

Tate Gallery
Millbank, SW1P 4RG (0171-887 8000).
National collection of British art from 16th century to present day including Turner Collection, as well as international 20th century painting and sculpture.

Victoria and Albert Museum
Cromwell Road, South Kensington, SW7 2RL (0171-938 8500).
Superb and extensive collections of the decorative arts, spanning 2000 years of international art and design. Arguably the most valuable single museum for any antique collector to visit. Regular exhibitions. The National Art Library is here.

Wallace Collection
Hertford House, Manchester Square, W1M 6BN (0171-935 0687).
One of the most important collections of European fine and decorative arts, displayed in the context of a grand private house. Particularly noted for French furniture and paintings by Boucher, Fragonard and Watteau, as well as the superb collection of Sevres porcelain. Frans Hals' 'Laughing Cavalier' is here, along with many fine Old Masters.

The Dictionary of Art

Table clock, Augsburg, silver-gilt and basse-taille enamel, c. 1570-75.
Case by Cornelius Gross, enamel by David Altenstetter.
(Kunsthistorisches Museum, Vienna). From the article GILDING

Two Craftsmen

6,700 Contributors

'As a reference work, there is nothing to compare with *The Dictionary of Art* .
People who work in the arts - lecturers, curators, dealers, researchers and journalists
- will find it is impossible to do their jobs without the magnificent resource now available to them'

Richard Dorment, Daily Telegraph, *14 December 1996*

MACMILLAN

Macmillan Publishers Ltd

For a free information pack

telephone: **+44 (0)171 881 8356**   fax: **+44 (0)171 881 8357**

ail: **tda@macmillan.co.uk**   web site: **http//www.groveartmusic.com**

YES I would like more information about *The Dictionary of Art*

Return to: **Emma Hardcastle,** *The Dictionary of Art,*
Macmillan Publishers Ltd., 25 Eccleston Place, London SW1W 9NF, UK.

Name _____

Address _____

Postcode _____   Country _____

Telephone _____   Fax _____

GH.97

A Tradition of Blending Substance with *Style*

TOWN & COUNTRY IS PROUD TO SUPPORT
THE GROSVENOR HOUSE ART & ANTIQUES FAIR

Pair of 'VASE PROU No. 2'
Manufacture Nationale de Sèvres, 1938
Porcelain vases by René Prou decorated by C. Fritz after a 1936 design of jockeys by R. Goujon
Height: 47 cms
Signed: *CF d'apr. ROLAND GOUJON 63.36*
From Le Pavillon de Sèvres Ltd. – the finest collection of 20th Century porcelain and ceramics
by La Manufacture Nationale de Sèvres.

Le Pavillon de Sèvres Ltd.

9 Halkin Arcade, Motcomb Street, London SW1X 8JT
Tel 0171-235 0937 Fax 0171-245 6341

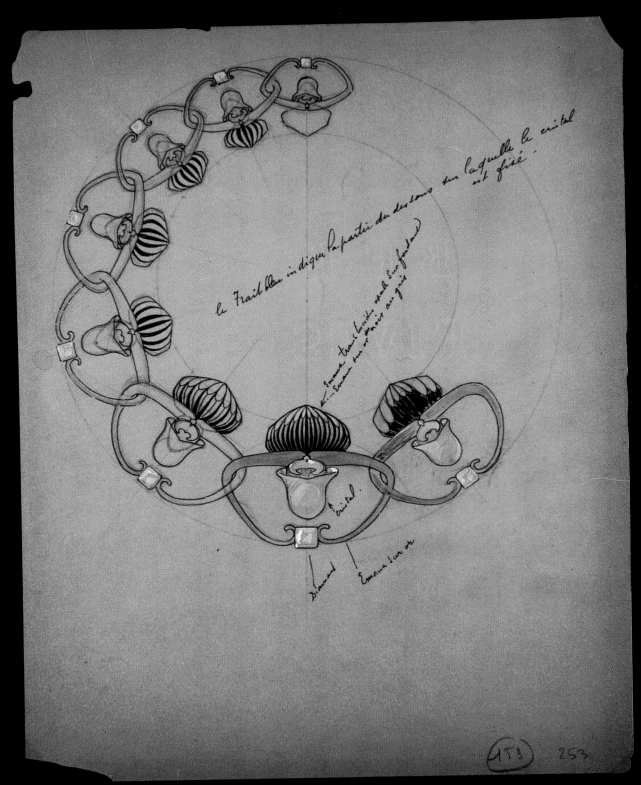

René Lalique design
COLLIER, ORCHIDÉES (ÉTUDE EN DEMI-MOTIFS)
Executed in Indian ink, gouache and watercolour on BFK Rives vegetable parchment

Height 28 cms   Width 22 cms

Galerie Moderne Ltd
10 Halkin Arcade · Motcomb Street · Belgravia · London SW1X 8JT
Tel: 0171 245 6907 · Fax: 0171 245 6341

TEFAF
BASEL 97

Information:
The European
Fine Art Foundation
+ 31 73 689 00 90

Monday – Friday
11am – 8pm
Saturday – Sunday
11am – 6pm

**International
Fine Art and Antiques Fair**

8 – 16 November 1997

Messe Basel, Switzerland

USEFUL ADDRESSES

The Grosvenor House Art & Antiques Fair
Organiser's Office, Grosvenor House,
Park Lane, London W1A 3AA
(0171-495 6406 or 0171-499 6363)

CONSERVATORS/RESTORERS

The BADA can advise (see under Trade
Associations). The following can give advice on
finding a qualified restorer in your area:

Association of British Picture Restorers
Station Avenue, Kew TW9 3QA
(0181-948 5644)

**British Antique Furniture
Restorers' Association**
The Old Rectory, Warmwell, Dorchester,
Dorset DT2 8HQ (01305-852104)

British Horological Institute
Upton Hall, Upton, Newark, Notts. NG23 5TE
(01636-813795)

British Watch and Clockmakers' Guild
West Wick, Marsh Road, Burnham-on-Crouch,
Essex CN0 8NE (01621-783104)

Institute of Paper Conservation
Leigh Lodge, Leigh, Worcester WR6 5LB
(01886-832323)

Museums and Galleries Commission
(Conservation Unit), 16 Queen Anne's Gate,
London SW1H 9AA (0171-233 3683)

Textile Conservation Centre
Apartment 22, Hampton Court Palace, East
Molesey, Surrey, KT8 9AU (0181-977 4943)
(qualified conservators undertaking work
themselves)

United Kingdom Institute for Conservation
6 Whitehorse Mews, Westminster Bridge Road,
London SE1 7QD (0171-620 3371)

EXPORT AND TAX MATTERS

Dept. of National Heritage
2-4 Cockspur Street, London SW1Y 5DH
(0171-211 6000) (re export licences)

Dept. of the Environment
Wildlife Trade Licensing Branch, Tollgate House,
Houlton Street, Bristol BS2 9DJ (0117-987 8202)
(re restrictions on export of material from
endangered species)

Local VAT offices - find under Customs and
Excise in the local telephone directory.

See also **BADA** and **LAPADA** under
Trade Associations.

TRADE ASSOCIATIONS

British Antique Dealers' Association (BADA)
20 Rutland Gate, London SW7 1BD
(0171-589 4128)

**LAPADA - The Association of Art
and Antique Dealers**,
535 Kings Road, Chelsea, London SW10 0SZ
(0171-823 3511)

**Incorporated Society of Valuers
and Auctioneers**
3 Cadogan Gate, London SW1X 0AS
(0171-235 2282)

Society of Fine Art Auctioneers
The Old Barracks, Sandon Road, Grantham,
Lincs NG31 9AS (01476-590176)

Society of London Art Dealers (SLAD)
91 Jermyn Street, London SW1Y 6JB
(0171-930 6137)

Antiquarian Booksellers Association
Sackville House, 40 Piccadilly, London W1V 9PA
(0171-439 3118)

Syndicat Nationale des Antiquaires
1 Bis, rue Clement-Marot, 75008 Paris
(33-1 47 20 31 87)

Thousands of collectors visit
Art on-line & Antiques on-line before they buy

Over five thousand people from around the world visit Corsellis-Montford's on-line services every day. If you are a gallery or a dealer, inclusion within either Art on-line or Antiques on-line could help you gain access to a new international market.

Once your stock and company details have been placed on-line, collectors can view your pages from anywhere in the world via the Internet. Any enquiries are forwarded directly to you.

Your stock page can be updated as often as you wish by phone, fax or by post and you can display as many images as you choose.

You do not need to have Internet access, only collectors wanting to view your information will require Internet access and the appropriate hardware.

For further details contact either
Georgie Mann
or
Orlando Plunket Greene
on +44 (0)171 370 0400

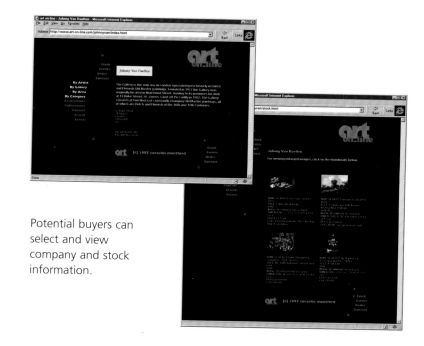

Potential buyers can select and view company and stock information.

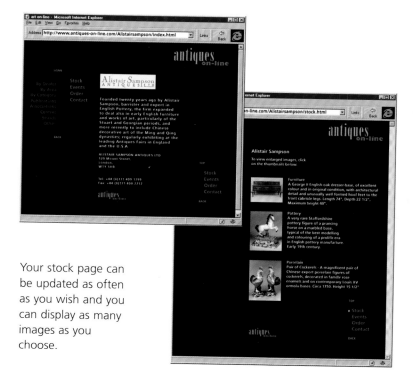

Your stock page can be updated as often as you wish and you can display as many images as you choose.

Art Dealers' Association of America
Inc, 575 Madison Avenue, New York, N.Y. 10022
(1-212 940 8590)

National Antique and Art Dealers'
Association of America
Inc, 12 East 56th Street, New York, N.Y.10022
(1-212 826 9707)

Art and Antique Dealers' League of
America, Inc
353 East 78th Street, New York, N.Y.10021
(1-212 879 7558)

Major London Auctioneers

Bonhams
Montpelier Street, Knightsbridge,
London SW7 1HH (0171-393 3900)

Christie's
8 King Street, London SW1Y 6QT
(0171-839 9060)

Christie's South Kensington
85 Old Brompton Road, London SW7 3LD
(0171-581 7611)

Phillips
101 New Bond Street, London W1Y 0AS
(0171-629 6602)

Sotheby's
34-35 New Bond Street, London W1A 2AA
(0171-493 8080)

Consultations and Advice:
See **Trade Associations**, also:

British Museum
Great Russell Street, London WC1B 3DG
(0171-636 1555).
Any afternoon, but appointment preferred.

National Gallery
Trafalgar Square, London WC2 (0171-306 0055).
Oil paintings may be brought to the gallery on
Wednesdays 2.30pm - 5 pm for an opinion.

National Portrait Gallery
St. Martin's Place, London WC2H 0HE
(0171-306 0055).
Portraits may be brought to the gallery every
Wenesday 2pm - 6 pm for an opinion. Alternatively,
a photograph and covering letter may be sent to the
NPG archive.

Tate Gallery
Millbank, London SW1 (0171-821 1313).
By post only; send a photographs to either the
Curators of the British Collection (for British
works up to the end of the 19th century), or the
Curators of the 20th Century Modern Collection,
as appropriate.

Victoria and Albert Museum
Cromwell Road, London SW7 2RL
(0171-938 8500).
Tuesday afternoons; contact the appropriate
department in advance.

Miscellaneous

English Heritage
23 Saville Row, London W1X 1AB
(0171-973 3000)

Furniture History Society
c/o Furniture and Woodwork Collection,
Victoria & Albert Museum, Cromwell Road,
London SW7 2RL (0171-938 8284)

Historic Houses Association
2 Chester Street, London SW1X 7BB
(0171-259 5688)

National Art Collections Fund
Millais House, 7 Cromwell Place,
London SW7 2JN (0171-225 4800)

National Trust
36 Queen Anne's Gate, London SW1H 9AS
(0171-222 9251)

The Worshipful Company of Goldsmiths
Goldsmiths' Hall, Foster Lane,
London EC2 6BN (0171-606 7010)

For business,
for pleasure,
for the world –
a welcome for you

FORTE
HOTELS

Forte and Le Méridien Hotels and Resorts bring you an exceptional range of hotels in Europe, the Americas, Asia, the Pacific and the Middle East.

For reservations and further information, call your local travel agent, or Forte on **0800 40 40 40.**

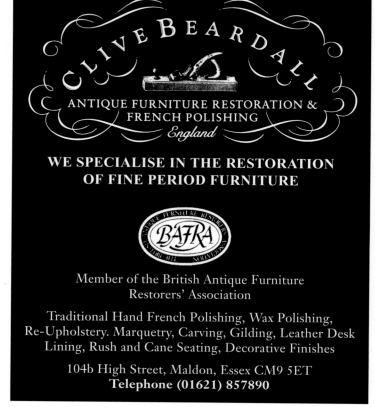

OLYMPIA LONDON

THE FINE ART and ANTIQUES FAIR

5~15 June 1997

17-23 November 1997

24 February ~ 1 March 1998

Come to Olympia to see 380 leading antique and fine art dealers from Britain, Europe and the United States. You can buy with confidence - all the antiques are scrutinised by independent experts to ensure each item is correctly identified.

◆

Serious collectors, treasure hunters and those delighted by the exotic and the unusual can search among fine furniture, longcase and bracket clocks, jewels and porcelain, the paintings, prints and watercolours, enamels, silver and glass, books and textiles.

◆

Fair information: The Olympia Antiques Fairs
P&O Events Limited, Exhibition Centre, Warwick Road, London SW5 9TA
Tel: (44) 171 370 8188/8186   Fax: (44) 171 370 8221   Email: olympia-antiques@eco.co.uk

Mrs James Gregory by Sir Henry Raeburn, circa 1798, The National Trust for Scotland, Fyvie Castle Collection

THE ROMANTIC GARDEN

NURSERY

SWANNINGTON NORWICH NORFOLK NR9 5NW
Tel: (01603) 261488   Fax: (01603) 871668

The Romantic Garden Nursery is situated 10 miles North West of
Norwich and Specialises in Topiary.

In addition to traditional evergreen topiary the nursery also stocks deciduous
topiary as well as large and specimen plants. Field grown Box and Yew
for hedging and developing your own topiary are available.

The nursery is situated in the heart of Norfolk, so if a personal visit is not possible,
this is not a problem as we deliver by carrier to all parts of the EC.

The nursery exhibits at many shows including The Chelsea Flower Show and
Hampton Court Palace Flower Show where we are pleased to meet you and talk about
your requirements and show you the quality of our plants. We are happy to visit you at
home and clip your own topiary or develop an existing plant into something.

Harpers & Queen

'LA TABLE DE CAMPAGNE'. OIL PAINTING BY HENRI LE SIDANER (1862–1939). FROM RICHARD GREEN. STAND 59.

STYLE
WITH SUBSTANCE